Ayrshire in the Age of Improvement

**contemporary accounts of agrarian and social improvement
in late eighteenth century Ayrshire**

edited by

David McClure

published by
Ayrshire Archaeological and Natural History Society
Ayr, 2002

printed by
The Cromwell Press, Trowbridge, Wiltshire

designed and typeset by David McClure

ISBN 0 9542253 0 9

Contents

Introduction

The two works reproduced in this book, by Andrew Wight – published in 1778 and 1784, and William Fullarton – published in 1793, are vivid and informative records of the condition of Ayrshire during a time when Scotland became "the most dynamically modernising society in Europe."[1] Against the background of the Enlightenment – a revolution in all fields of thought – came the improvement, a practical revolution founded in agriculture, but leading to new roads, better housing, growth of towns and villages, the burgeoning of old industries and the foundation of new ones.

By the fourth quarter of the eighteenth century, improvement of agriculture in Scotland had become a national obsession. This was a pivotal point in the great transition between a peasant, subsistence agriculture – unchanged in 1750 in most of Scotland – and the productive, market–orientated agriculture that became the envy of Europe. It was then that improvement ceased to be the concern of a few pioneers risking their own fortunes, and of gentlemanly societies that debated much and improved little, and became a necessity for every self–respecting landowner.

Before improvement, agriculture in Scotland was characterised by short leases, giving no incentive to the tenant to improve either the land or the buildings; rack rents and servitudes, which kept the tenants at best just above starvation; and overcropping and absence of fallowing, which impoverished the soil and kept yields low, again maintaining the tenant at a bare subsistence level at best. Fullarton pictured the county as it was around 1750: "farm–houses were mere hovels, moated with clay, having an open hearth or fire–place in the middle; the dunghill at the door; the cattle starving; and the people wretched."[2] Mere tracks served for roads, and there were few wheeled carts.

With improvement came long leases, usually 19 years and often with renewal at the same rent guaranteed, so that the tenant would remain to enjoy the benefit of his labour; enclosed fields, so that the cattle could be kept off the land when wet or during the growing season; the introduction of turnips for feeding cattle and sheep, and of potatoes for feeding people; use of grass seed, to improve pasture; rotation of crops, interspersed with fallow years, so that the ground was not impoverished, and crop yields became higher; selective breeding, to raise the quality of stock; use of lime and dung to improve the soil. These and many other concerns will be seen in the words of Wight and Fullarton as they travel around Ayrshire, praising here and criticising there.

After Culloden, and the brutal suppression of the Jacobites, the government moved to improve the circumstances of the Highlanders, to make them less likely to be rebellious in future. This was the work of the Commissioners of the Annexed

Estates, who administered those estates, mostly in the Highlands, which were confiscated after the 1745 rebellion from landowners who had supported the Young Pretender, Bonnie Prince Charlie.[3] It was many years later and with much, they thought, already achieved in this direction, that the commissioners instructed an East Lothian tenant farmer, Andrew Wight, to tour Scotland and report back on the best farming practices, so that they could be applied in the Annexed Estates. Wight owed his nomination for the task to Henry Home, Lord Kames, one of the commissioners and the author of a recent work on improvement, *The gentleman farmer, Being an attempt to improve agriculture, by subjecting it to the test of rational principles,* published in Edinburgh and London in 1776. So useful were Wight's reports that, before his work was half done, it was decided that they should be published, in order that the knowledge could be spread throughout the Kingdom, for the instruction of all. Wight surveyed all the mainland counties of Scotland, with the exception of Argyll, and his surveys appeared, in six books, in 1778 and 1784.

In 1718, the then proprietor of the Ormiston estate in East Lothian, Lord Cockburn, had granted Andrew Wight's grandfather, Robert, a 38 year lease of Muirhouse farm, on which he was already a tenant, renewable on certain terms for further periods of 19 years.[4] Cockburn was one of a select few later accorded the title "father of Scottish agriculture." He was certainly a pioneer, and corresponded with his gardener and tenants on the latest ideas in agriculture. In 1724, Robert Wight was probably the first tenant farmer in Scotland to cultivate turnips in drills. Cockburn sent the sons of his tenants, among them Alexander Wight, to England to learn from the improvements already introduced there. Later, in the 1750s, Alexander was brought over to Ayrshire by Alexander Montgomerie, 10th Earl of Eglinton, so that the successful practices of East Lothian could be transferred to his estate; as Fullarton put it, "to introduce the proper mode of ploughing, levelling ridges, fallowing, drilling, turnip husbandry, and rotations of crop."[5]

Cockburn was an unhappy exemplar. He over–reached himself with the creation of the village of Ormiston, and had to sell his estate. The purchaser, the Earl of Hopetoun, the Wights' new landlord, became one of the Commissioners of the Annexed Estates and, if not instrumental in the selection of Andrew Wight, would have been in a good position to know his worth.

Andrew Wight surveyed and reported with all the confidence of one born and raised on a farm that had been in the forefront of improvement in Scotland for fifty years. He commented on practices good and bad, and stated his conclusions and opinions in a plain fashion: "The operations of William Jackson, another of Sir Adam's tenants, have every appearance of good husbandry, regularly conducted."[6] He thought that progress required the close interest of the landowner: "Every operation depending on activity of servants, will be expeditious in proportion to the activity of the master. This gentleman makes it a rule to be at the head of every thing himself."[7] He sympathised with local difficulties: "the water of Lugar is a troublesome neighbour."[8] He gave praise where praise was due: "Lady Dumfries … is the very soul of husbandry and manufactures in that part of the country."[9] He cast his eye over villages and towns, whose growth and industry was to provide markets for the higher yields of improved fields: "*Girvan* is a clean little town, and the inhabitants industrious and thriving, particularly the shoemakers, who tan their own leather, and make shoes for America, which are carried to Glasgow."[10] Lord Kames had advised his fellow Commissioners well, and Andrew Wight's lucid report makes fascinating reading today.

In contrast to Andrew Wight, Colonel William Fullarton of Fullarton was a gentleman landowner, with all that that implied in wealth, family connections and education. As he was an Ayrshire man, a Biographical Note, contributed by Rob Close, has been included in this volume (page 66).

Colonel Fullarton's breadth of learning and extensive travels were reflected in his report. But it was also informed by the sixteen years that had passed since Wight's first survey of Ayrshire, and all that had happened during that time. Symon lists 18 books on agricultural topics that were published in Scotland in that period, not including *The Statistical Account of Scotland,* the first volumes of which appeared in 1791.[11] Most of the Ayrshire accounts were available to Fullarton, as may be seen from the Statistical Summary which he abstracted from them.[12] During the intervening years much had been achieved: "there is no country in Europe, where men, possessing property in land, have so generally applied their skill and capital, to the encouragement of husbandry, and the introduction of new modes of cultivation."[13] Most of the principle roads had been turnpiked, and were suitable for carts and carriages. And there were new industries: in particular, the tarworks and ironworks at Muirkirk, and the cotton mills at Catrine, and new houses built to accommodate the workers.

If there were achievements to be trumpeted, there were also alarms to be raised. Subsistence peasants may have gone from the fermtouns, but in their place were workers in villages and towns, all too ready to absorb radical notions. The horrors of the French Revolution were an ever–present warning of the danger of complacency: "the signal calamities, accumulated on the landed proprietors of a neighbouring and distracted nation," though these could be happily ascribed to the French landowners' neglect of their estates and the consequent distress of the peasantry.[14] Higher rents were the reward of improvement for the landowner; there had to be a sufficient share of the produce for the tenant farmer to improve his condition. Landowners owed "their first duties and attentions to their tenants and estates."[15]

"Don't neglect horse–howing if you love Scotland." What better captures the spirit of patriotism that attached to improvement than this advice, the postscript in a letter written by Alexander Montgomerie, 10th Earl of Eglinton, to his brother

Archibald? Alexander was about to fight a duel. With a real fear for his life, he asked his brother to honour his memory and "to execute ... what I should have done if I had time."[16]

In annotating this book, the intention has been to provide brief explanations of what may be unfamiliar, and to suggest possibilities for further reading. The editor wishes to acknowledge the very considerable contribution, which Rob Close made to this task, as also the many notes from Bill Layhe, whose experience is particularly relevant to the subject matter. There was also an invaluable contribution from Alastair Hendry, who translated Fullarton's many Latin quotations. He has corrected the references given by Fullarton, which were often misleading or incorrect. He has identified sources where Fullarton did not provide them, and in these instances the information is given after the translations. Rob Close applied his patient and painstaking proof–reading talents to the entire text. Any remaining errors, typographical or of fact, are the editor's.

The transcriptions were made from the original texts. Wight's *Present State of Husbandry* was consulted in Glasgow University Library and Fullarton's *General View of the Agriculture of the County of Ayr* in the Scottish and Local History Library, Carnegie Library, Ayr (South Ayrshire Libraries). The editor acknowledges with thanks the assistance of the staff of both institutions.

The footnotes of the original authors are identified by *o.f.* and *Original footnote*. In the case of Fullarton, whose footnotes were many and in some cases long, they have been inserted into the body of the text, indented and identified as above. The subheadings in the transcription of Wight's work have been inserted by the editor; in the case of Fullarton they are his own.

The spelling of the original authors has been retained, except in the case of obvious typographical errors, which have been corrected. Two changes, however, were made to conform to modern typography and practice: the old long s, similar to f, has been replaced by s; and £, s and d have been used throughout for sums of money.

Finally, acknowledgement is made of one of the society's own publications, from which the "Directory of Ayrshire" and the "Gazetteer of Ayrshire", both 1750–1800, provided information about the individual landowners and estates mentioned in the text: Strawhorn, John, ed., *Ayrshire at the Time of Burns*, Ayr, 1959; generally abbreviated *ATB*. This was Vol. 5 in *Ayrshire Collections* (AANHS).

Sketch Map of Ayrshire Parishes

Key to Parishes

Cunninghame (16)	Key No.	Kyle (21)	Key No.
Ardrossan	7	Auchinleck	28
Beith	5	Ayr	29
Dalry	4	Coylton	3
Dreghorn	13	Craigie	21
Dunlop	6	Dalmellington	40
Fenwick	10	Dalrymple	35
Irvine	12	Dundonald	17
Kilbirnie	2	Galston	19
Kilmarnock	15	Mauchline	24
Kilmaurs	14	Monkton & Prestwick	22
Kilwinning	8	Muirkirk	26
Largs	1	New Cumnock	33
Loudoun	16	Newton–upon–Ayr	29a
Stevenston	11	Ochiltree	31
Stewarton	9	Old Cumnock	32
West Kilbride	3	Riccarton	18
		St. Quivox	29b
Carrick (9)		Sorn	25
Ballantrae	44	Stair	27
Barr	42	Symington	20
Colmonell	43	Tarbolton	23
Dailly	38		
Girvan	39		
Kirkmichael	36		
Kirkoswald	37		
Maybole	34		
Straiton	41		

The parishes have been numbered as in the *Third Statistical Account of Scotland: Ayrshire*, Strawhorn, John and Boyd, William, eds., 1951. Newton–upon–Ayr and St. Quivox had before then become part of Ayr parish. They are shown separately here, numbered 29a and 29b respectively.

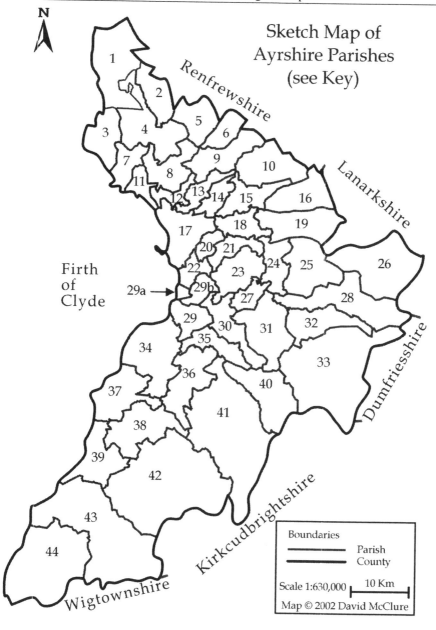

N

Sketch Map of
Ayrshire Parishes
(see Key)

Renfrewshire

Lanarkshire

Firth
of
Clyde

29a →

Dumfriesshire

Kirkcudbrightshire

Wigtownshire

Boundaries

Parish
County

Scale 1:630,000   10 Km

Map © 2002 David McClure

PRESENT STATE

OF

HUSBANDRY

IN

SCOTLAND.

EXTRACTED

FROM REPORTS MADE TO THE COMMISSIONERS

OF THE ANNEXED ESTATES,

AND PUBLISHED BY THEIR AUTHORITY.

IN TWO VOLUMES.

VOLUME I.

EDINBURGH:

Printed for W. STRAHAN, and T. CADELL, London; and W. CREECH, Edinburgh.

MDCCLXXVIII.

Title page (actual page size 4 $^5/_8$ by 8 $^1/_8$ inches)

Present State of Husbandry in Scotland

by Andrew Wight[17]

List of the Honourable, The Commissioners of the Annexed Estates.

Agreeable to the order of their Nominations.[18]

Earl of Marchmont	Lord Stonefield
Earl of Hopeton	Mansfield Cardonnel, Esq.
Rt. Hon. James Steuart–Mackenzie	Robert Oliphant, Esq.
Hon. Charles Hope–Weir, Esq.	George Clerk–Maxwell, Esq.
Lord President	Lord Elliock
Lord Chief Baron	Duke of Argyle
Lord Justice Clerk	Earl of Galloway
Mr Baron Maule	Sir Adolphus Oughton
Lord Kames	Thomas Dundas, Esq.
George Wynne, Esq.	Captain Archibald Grant
Lord Advocate	Major General Græme
Lord Gardenstoun	Duke of Buccleugh
Lord Hailes	Lord Ankerville
John Swinton, Esq.	Solicitor General

Wm Barclay, Secretary

J. Morison, Principal Clerk

INSTRUCTIONS by the Commissioners of the Annexed estates to Mr Andrew Wight, for a particular inspection and survey of the corn–farms of the Annexed Estates.[19]

1. To take inspection of the different soils in these farms.
2. To inquire diligently into the method of culture, and to examine the instruments of husbandry.
3. To inquire into the different grains that are commonly sown, the quantity sown on each acre, and the product.
4. What is the manure commonly used. And what manure there may be access to.
5. To take an account of the climate and seasons.
6. The price of labour and provisions.
7. With respect to the very different farms, whether it be most profitable to labour with horses or oxen, or with a part of both.
8. How the farms lie with respect to markets for disposing of the product.

9. A critical article expected is, to propose methods of culture the best suited to the different farms; and the best models of instruments of husbandry.

10. To have in view green provender for the spring in every farm.

And, in general, Mr Wight is desired to attend to every article that may give light to the Commissioners in the management of the Annexed Estates.

Jo. Campbell, Pres.

Preface[20]

The chief motive for naming Commissioners to manage the Annexed Estates, was to civilize the people of those estates, and by kind treatment to make them good subjects. This motive has been so fully accomplished by the prudent management of the Commissioners, that his Majesty has not at present more affectionate subjects.

The Commissioners have attempted a farther reformation, which is, to lead on gradually the tenants to improve their husbandry, which has hitherto been at a very low ebb. In that view, a careful Survey of the different estates, and of each farm in particular, was found necessary; for how could any instructions be given with certainty, without knowledge of the soil, of the method of culture, of the instruments of husbandry, and of many other particulars? The difficulty was, to find a person equal to the truth, not only intelligent, but faithful. Mr Andrew Wight, farmer at Ormeston, was suggested, and approved of as unexceptionable. The honour of being thought worthy to execute so important a task, made him chearfully accept. The Board found so much benefit from his two first Surveys, which were confined to the Annexed Estates, as to make them judge, that a more general Survey would be an acceptable present to the public; and they rejoice, that at a trifling expence, they can be useful to their country in its chief concern, the improvement of agriculture.

This happens fortunately to be the critical time for such a survey. While the bulk of our farmers are creeping in the beaten path of miserable husbandry, without knowing better, or even wishing to know better, several men of genius, shaking off the fetters of custom, have traced out new paths for themselves, and have been successful, even beyond expectation. But their success has hitherto produced few imitators: so far from it, that among their slovenly neighbours they are reckoned giddy–headed projectors. A survey of what has been done by these spirited improvers meeting with the approbation of the Honourable Board, and a comparison of their mode of agriculture with the old, cannot fail to set them in so distinguished a light, as to induce many to follow their example. The great profits made by them, compared with what is common, must rouse our farmers to activity and imitation. If this motive prevail not, it is not easy to say what can prevail. Many ingenious farmers, dissatisfied with the common practice, would gladly attempt new modes; but are restrained by the uncertainty of success. Here they

will meet with encouragement from the success of others, which, removing their
scruples, will make them go on boldly, without fear of disappointment. Nor need
they be at any loss in the choice of the best modes: for in this publication they may
receive ample instruction, without going abroad for it; and every farmer who
wishes to be rich, has here the means chalked out to him.

The present work will produce another good effect. Persons of skill and
enterprise, who have advanced the art of husbandry, living at a distance, and
unconnected, have little opportunity to learn from each other. This work, by
collecting the experience of all into one view, will bestow upon each the
experience of all, and ripen them in their favourite art. No other means will
contribute so effectively to establish a complete system of husbandry. Fifty years
ago a survey of this kind would have been of no avail; because our practice,
cramped by custom, was the same everywhere; and there was nothing to be
learned. Fifty years hence, the knowledge and practice of husbandry will probably
be spread every where, and nothing will remain to be learned.

Besides, there can be no emulation among artists widely distant, where no
one knows what is passing among the rest. In this publication several eminent
farmers are brought into one group; and every one has access to know what is
passing among the rest. Emulation is kindled as between artists in close
neighbourhood, and each endeavours to excel.

It would be unpardonable to be silent upon the kind reception Mr Wight,
acting under the Commissioners, met with from many expert farmers, gentlemen
and others, who showed the greatest zeal to advance the reputation of their art, by
explaining to him every article of their practice. The Commissioners give them
thanks, and the Nation is indebted to them for much good instruction.

A note by Andrew Wight concerning measures[21]

The Linlithgow or Lothian measure for corn, the Scotch pint, and Scotch
acre, are always to be understood in this work, except it is otherwise expressed.

	Cubic inches
The Linlithgow or Lothian wheat and pease[22] firlot contains	2197.34
Ditto firlot for bear[23] or oats	3205.54
The Winchester bushel	2150.42

Hence, Four Winchester bushels are equal to three firlots three pecks and
seventy hundredth parts of a peck of wheat or pease, Linlithgow measure; and six
Winchester bushels of oats or barley are equal to one boll or four firlots and fifteen
hundredth parts of a peck of Linlithgow measure.

The Scotch pint is somewhat less than four English pints. The wheat–firlot contains twenty–one and one fourth Scotch pints; and the bear–firlot contains thirty–one of the same.

Four Scotch acres are somewhat less than five English acres.

Extracts from Andrew Wight's surveys

[Andrew Wight made two surveys of Ayrshire, reported in volume III part I, pages 149 to 287. The following is a complete transcription.]

AYRSHIRE

This country offers to the diligent inquirer a very busy and very agreeable scene. The activity of many gentlemen in husbandry improvements, and the extent of their improvements of late years, merit an ample reward, which a grateful soil never with–holds from a judicious cultivator who bestows liberally on his operations.

Glen App and Ballantrae

My entry to this county was by Glenap, a narrow vale between high hills, mostly green, partly heath, extremely proper for a sheep walk. Among the many little tenants in the vale, I found none that had either knowledge or inclination to improve their situation. Each of them have a few black cattle and a few small sheep; but the tenants are many, and the whole stocks together are far too numerous for the pasture; whence both tenants and stock are starved, and little gained for paying the landlord's rent. These tenants, however, are so far improved, as to salve lightly, which produces ten shillings for the stone of wool, inferior, however, to the price in Galloway for the same sort of sheep, owing probably to the high ground and stormy climate. From Glenap to Ballantrae, a rough coarse country, hill and heath, and none residing in it who so much as think of making a single step out of the common road. From Ballantrae, a nest of smugglers, to Girvan, I met with nothing worth observation till I came to Ardmillan. The proprietor, Mr Crawford, has attended to his interest.[24] Pasture is his object, which has led him to inclose with stone walls even the hilly ground. Every thing around him has an agreeable aspect.

Girvan

Girvan is a clean little town, and the inhabitants industrious and thriving, particularly the shoemakers, who tan their own leather, and make shoes for America, which are carried to Glasgow. The village and lands around belong to Mr Hamilton of Bargeny.[25] Most of the inhabitants have built neat houses for themselves, on land leased to them for hundreds of years, in all respects equal to property. This is a much better method, both for landlord and tenant, than feuing.

The latter is a most intolerable burden on small property, and throws the poor people into the hands of most rapacious scriveners, who, every thirty or forty years, draw from them the value at least of their property. A lease, on the contrary, is transmitted to heirs and singular successors, without any expence, which entitles the landlord to draw more rent than a farmer can afford to pay. The soil, being light and sharp, is easily managed, which is a great comfort to poor manufacturers. They have sea weed in abundance, which is their chief manure. As soon as any quantity comes to shore, the women carry it on their backs, and put it in small coils like hay, where it is to be used for the potatoe crop. When the potatoe season approaches, it is spread out to be dried, and then put on the ground. The men are thus left to carry on their own business. They have few horses, and these are employed in tilling. The potatoes are all planted in drills, the sea weed being put into the furrow. Bear follows, next oats, and then again potatoes. Every crop is good, and the industry of the people rewarded. No rent is better paid; and there is a great number of acres thus occupied.

Bargany

The estate of Bargeny contains at least 30,000 acres, whereof 1200 are arable, or capable to be made so. What is not arable feeds black cattle and sheep. The last might be turned to great account by proper management of pasture, and to still greater, were any rational attempt made to improve the sheep and the wool.

Mr Hamilton, by a chearful and kindly behaviour, has the choice of the best farmers; to these he gives long leases, and, by his own practice, teaches them the best method of improvement. Upon any complaint of a hard bargain, it is a rule that gentlemen never bind a poor tenant to his ruin, and accordingly sets him free. Tho' this, I am convinced, be done from a motive of humanity and compassion; yet, I am far from being certain but that Mr Hamilton will upon the whole, be a gainer even in point of interest. Not only will the best tenants flock to him, but will be frank in their efforts, when they know they cannot be substantially hurt.

Lime–stone and coal are found in this estate, and Mr Hamilton is working both for his own interest and that of the neighbourhood.

Some time ago the roads were so bad as not to admit the smallest wheel carriage. This public spirited gentleman has been very diligent in getting good roads made; and for that purpose has contributed out of his own pocket no less than £500 Sterling; a rare instance, but well deserving to be imitated. One immediate reward his patriotism has procured him, which is, to increase considerably the demand for his coal and lime.

His low lands lie on both sides of Girvan water, mostly dry, and a good mixed soil of earth and gravel. But here I avoid entering into particulars; for, though the culture is carried on in the approved method, yet there is nothing singular to afford any new instruction. The only article I venture to criticise is that of grass seeds sown with barley; three pounds red clover, six white, three yellow, three rib–wort, and two bushels ryegrass. What I object to is his small quantity of red clover, where hay is intended for the first crop: Better far to with–hold one bushel of ryegrass, and the yellow clover totally, which will afford space for six or seven pounds more of red clover, as without that quantity the hay crop must be very scanty.

The most laborious part is to bring into tilth the higher grounds covered with heath and full of large stones. But it was a great temptation to bestow labour and money, to find the under stratum of this muir a good soil upon a dry bottom. The ground has been entirely cleared of stones, the large ones blasted, in order to admit the plough.[26] It is ploughed and cross ploughed, limed and formed into ridges 15 feet broad, directed so to carry off the water. Being thus brought into tilth, it is cropped with judgement, according to the nature of the soil. The rent of this land, in the state of nature, was under fifteen pence *per* acre. Upon what is improved as above, he put a rent from 10s to 13s 4d; and if he persevere, of which there can be no doubt where the profit is so great, he will leave a great estate to his heirs, and at the same time enrich the country.

Much ground is planted by Mr Hamilton, both for ornament and shelter, which, with the old plantations, make a fine appearance.

I am glad to find the dawn of good husbandry beginning to peep out here among the tenants. *John Johnston* makes some figure in tillage, in liming, and grass–seeds.[27] He was encouraged by Mr Hamilton with a substantial dwelling–house and proper offices. Others copying from him are doing better than formerly. *Gavin Park,* a young man, stimulated by the success of some of his neighbours, has taken a large farm from Sir John Cathcart, and shows a good spirit in his operations.[28]

It is very discouraging that Mr Hamilton hitherto has not succeeded with his tenants in the hilly parts of his estate to attempt any reformation on their sheep. To improve their numerous flocks, were it but a shilling *per* head, would produce a very large sum. As I passed along in my way to Kilkerran, I was delighted to see corn and clover fields in excellent order, and hedges growing vigorously, all done by Mr Thomson minister at Dalry [*sic:* Dailly], a man of an amiable character.[29] The land belongs to Sir Adam Fergusson.[30] The operations of William Jackson, another of Sir Adam's tenants, have every appearance of good husbandry, regularly conducted. Good example is infectious as well as bad; and there is no reason to doubt but that these gentlemen will be imitated.

Kilkerran

On a nearer approach to Kilkerran, a narrow, but pleasant valley, of a good soil, opens to view. There, in different fields, I saw various operations of husbandry carried on with industry and attention. The inclosures in perfection, both hedges and stone walls. Lime is the only manure used. I saw a number of sheep in a large inclosure opposite to the house, of different kinds, Dorchester, Cully,[31] Bakewell,[32] and also the breed of the country. Sir Adam was from home. I was much disappointed, as I reckoned upon accurate information from Sir Adam, of the different branches of improvement carrying on briskly here. But this disappointment is amply made up by a letter I had the honour to receive from him, which gives a very accurate, and no less satisfactory, account of the progress of agriculture in that part of the country, chiefly owing to Sir Adam himself. I should think it criminal to with–hold this letter from the public, though I was not permitted to enter it into my report. Modesty is a pleasing virtue, but I have no notion that it should entitle a man to hide his more active and more eminent virtues.

"Kilkerran, Sept. 26, 1777.
"Sir,
"I have the favour of your letter, and am exceedingly sorry that I was so unfortunate as to be absent when you called at this place in your progress through this part of the country. I not only regret it on my own account, but because I should have been glad to have contributed to your obtaining such information as might have promoted the plan of the trustees; which I could have done more effectually when present, than by any thing I can write in the compass of a letter."

"With regard to this part of the country, if you never was in it before, you would, no doubt, observe much in general to find fault with—a great deal of land uncultivated, and the culture of other parts very imperfect. But if you had been here some years ago, and compare the state it was then in with that in which it is in now, you cannot fail to have remarked a very great alteration. To me, who remembers this country when there was scarce an enclosure in it but some few round the gentlemen's houses, when there was not a pound of grass seed sown in it from one end of it to the other, and when the whole attention of the farmer, and the whole dung of the farm, were applied to a few acres, while the rest was totally neglected, the difference is very striking."

"With regard to myself, my object has been to turn the farm in my own possession into good grass as soon as possible; and the whole use I have made of the plough has been with a view to that. The trouble and expence that I have bestowed on this object has been much greater than any person would conceive from the quantity of ground that I have improved, without considering what it was in its natural state. You cannot have failed to observe the multitude of large stones upon the uncultivated fields in this country; most of these are of such a size that they require to be blasted with gun–powder before they are carried off. As the soil runs naturally to wood, there is a necessity of clearing the fields of shrubs and bushes before they can be properly ploughed. If to this is added the expence of draining, you will not be surprised at my saying that many fields cost more than their original price before the plough is put into the ground. That particular field which you observed as sown down with grass this season, was, when I began with it, so remarkably covered with stones, as to make it a matter of wonder how the tenant could contrive to plow it at all; yet now there is not a stone upon it so large as your fist. After clearing the ground, my practice is to lime it on the grass; in doing which, we *compute* the lime laid on to be about an hundred bolls to the Scots acre; though, as I have the lime within my own farm, and am not under the necessity of measuring it, as I should be, were I to buy it, I cannot answer for the perfect accuracy of the computation. I then take two crops of oats off it. The third year I fallow it carefully, and in the spring following dung it well, and sow it down with barley and grass seeds. Where the land is not intended for being continued in hay, the grass seeds I sow are ryegrass and white clover, which I cut the first year, and afterwards throw it out into pasture. I am sensible that two crops of oats running is not the best husbandry; but oats being the hardiest grain, and answering better than any other while the land is rough, and not properly broke, it is for this reason that I follow the method I have mentioned. The only variations I have made from this method are, that sometimes I take a crop of pease instead of the second crop of oats; if the land is cleaner of stones than usual, I have sometimes sown turnip in the following year; and some once or twice, I took wheat instead of barley the last year. But, though that has answered with me, I do not approve of it, as the land is apt to become so stiff in the winter, that it cannot be sufficiently opened in the spring to receive the grass seed, without destroying the wheat. I sometimes also sow down with oats instead of barley."[33]

"I have mentioned to you that my object is to get my land, as soon as possible, into good grass. I am partly led to this from a desire to have as much dressed land round my house as I can. But, independent of this consideration, I am convinced it is better adapted to the climate of this country than tillage."

"Though the land in Carrick (of which I wish all along to be understood to speak) is of a lighter nature than the other districts of Ayrshire, and in many places has a dry gravelly bottom, yet the rains in spring and harvest are very unfavourable for raising corn. It has, at the same time, such a tendency to grass, that, except for the first and second year, provided it be made rich enough, it will shoot up pasture almost as good without sowing as with it. For these reasons, joined to the great steepness and irregularity of the surface, I consider grass and not corn to be the proper crop for this country."

"With regard to cattle, of which a great number are bred for the English market in this country, they are pretty much the same with the Galloway breed, mostly hummelt.[34] They are very hardily bred, being never in a house (except such as are intended for milk), and when put into good pasture, they rise to a great size."

"With regard to sheep, of which a great number are bred on the high grounds, I am apt to believe that they are not so well understood as the black cattle. Considerable attention has, however, been bestowed of late on mending the breed of sheep. A number of gentlemen have brought in sheep from England, and the farmers are sensible of the importance of mending the breed, by procuring good rams. I have, however, great doubts how far it even will be practicable to introduce the English sheep into our hills. In the low and sheltered grounds, they answer very well; and the advantage, particularly with respect to the wool, is very great. But on the high and exposed mountains, I am persuaded they would not answer. The utmost length that I think we should be safe to go, would be to endeavour to raise our own breed by a mixture with the English; and even that should be done with great caution."

"The only part of your letter that, I think, remains unanswered, is what relates to the tenants. Now, although I have several tenants who deserve commendation for their industry and attention, yet I cannot say that there is any one who has made himself so remarkable as deserves being particularly mentioned. What I have said of the expense attending the improvement of land here, will show how difficult it must be for any man, without a great stock, to carry it very far. But though I cannot name any tenant in particular, yet I can say in general, that there is a remarkable alteration to the better, both in their knowledge and management, since I began to attend to country affairs. Many of them had an aversion to have their lands enclosed; whereas now, no farmer, such as I would choose to have for a tenant, will take a lease, unless the lands are enclosed; the consequence of which is, that if I live three or four years, every arable farm I have will be enclosed. They are all getting into the practice, more or less, of sowing grass seeds; and instead of running out their lands, by ploughing them up as soon as they are fit to produce a poor crop of corn, as was the practice formerly, they are now sensible of the importance of having them in good heart; and the distinction of croft and field land, except among some of the poorest sort, is, in a manner, entirely abolished."

Cloncaird

Mr *Whiteford of Dunduff,* a spirited farmer, applies himself with skill and industry to improve his estate, originally a moor covered with heath, naturally dry, or made so by art.[35] Lime is his great fund for improvement, to which he has added shell–marl lately discovered. To get his fields into grass is his chief aim; because, in a rainy country, as this is, corn is but a precarious crop.

He deals in turnip, cabbage, and kail, in drills; but in new ground paired and burnt, turnip is sowed broadcast, and eat with sheep on the field. Carrot is also sowed broadcast. And this curious improver has also ventured on saintfoine and lucerne in drills, nine inches asunder, and handhoed.[36]

Here is a fine wood of timber–trees on the banks of a river.[37] Several new plantations are added of fir and other timber. There is a neat barn floored with bricks at both ends laid in sand, the one for storing the corn, in order to be threshed, the other to hold the grain. This method deserves to be imitated.

He uses the chain–plough drawn by two horses.

Wages in this part of the country are moderate. A labourer constantly employed gets eightpence *per* day, and there are plenty of them, which is a favourable circumstance for carrying on the operations of husbandry.

As I approached toward Kirkmichael, art and good husbandry appeared, and the marks grew stronger near the village. A rich crop of hay, good pasture, oats, bear, pease better than ordinary, and potatoes in drills. The minister was the operator.[38]

Maybole

I passed on to Maybole, where there is good soil ill managed, and yet, by dung from the town, produces now and then weighty crops. The minister and Bailie Pyper must be excepted, who summer fallow regularly, give dung, sow bear or barley with grass seeds, red clover 18 pounds, ryegrass four bushels *per* acre.[39] It is a pity that such willing improvers should be taught that half the quantity of ryegrass would answer as well. They get, however, from 200 to 300 stone of hay *per* acre, the stone being 24 pounds English. Hay is taken three years, after which fallow as before. Wheat is also interspersed. Such severe cropping requires better soil than is to be found around Maybole; but it would appear that they trust greatly to the town's dung. When the demand for that commodity increases by more improvers, these two gentlemen, it is to be hoped, will reform their practice, and be more cautious not to run out their ground.

Newark

Captain Kennedy near this place is an intelligent farmer, especially as to the management of sheep.[40] He possesses an inclosure of 800 acres in Carrick–muir, his own property, surrounded with a good stone dike. In this inclosure 1200 sheep pasture, summer and winter, without getting any dry food, not even in the severest weather. Yet it is a high ground; but much of it is hilly, which affords shelter; and being close to the sea, no snow lies. At his entry in 1764, the flock on the ground was valued at £5 *per* score with their wool on, including all kinds, ewes with their lambs, hogs, and dimmonts three years old.[41] To improve this flock, Tweedmuir and Carrick were searched for the best rams; and, by crossing and recrossing with the original stock, a considerable reform was made in a few years. His stock would now sell for double the valuation above mentioned. His three years old wedders sell at 12 shillings in November or December.[42] His stock are now of the hardy black–faced kind, a short body, a good shape, and not long in the leg. To try the effect of smearing, he made the following experiment. He reserved from smearing, several years," ten or twelve sheep of his flock, which were the whole time inferior to the rest of the flock, both in flesh and wool. They were longer of taking on fat, and the wool was hairier, coarser, and harder. Mr Kennedy informed me of a race of small sheep bred at Dunart in the parish of Maybole, that carry very fine wool.[43] Their pasture is on a range of hills on the sea coast. The grass indeed is fine, nor is the climate very cold. The wool commonly sells at 15 shillings *per* stone. I was also told by this gentlemen of one John McKie at Tarryfessoch, who farms more than 13,000 acres of hill land belonging to the Earl of Cassillis.[44] His rent is £150, and he paid £1000 of grassum for a nineteen years lease. The same man possesses 1400 acres from Lord Galloway.[45] This is a bold undertaking; but, as I am told, he has spirit and industry equal to it.

Improvements on this side of the country are going on apace. The Earl of Cassillis leads the way, and his tenants creep on the best way they can after him. When the spirit becomes more general, emulation will accelerate their motion.

Culzean

When I passed by Cullean, the Earl of Cassillis's, I was wet through all my clothes with a heavy and constant fall of rain, which obliged me to push forward to Ayr; and by this unfortunate accident, I missed seeing the Earl's improvements.[46] To make up that loss, I prevailed on Captain Kennedy to procure from Mr Bulley, the Earl's operator in improvements, a full state of all his operations at Cullean, which he has given in a very distinct and accurate manner, that shows his attention and abilities in the improvements of husbandry.[47] The public, I think, will be instructed by it.

"Cullean, Feb. 6, 1778.
"Sir,
"I received your letter in August last, inquiring into the state of the Earl of Cassillis's improvements at this place, which I should have answered sooner, but was dissatisfied that you did not come this length when you was so near as Maybole; as you would then have seen that it was impossible in so short a time as I have been here, to have got into a regular culture and course of crops; and therefore could not give you that information which seems to have been the intention of your inquiries. However, as Captain Kennedy informs me that you have lately wrote him that you wished to hear from me, I here send you an account of my operations so far as I have gone; but, in the first place, shall describe the nature of the soil, and the condition I found it in."[48]

"I came here in December 1773, when I entered into the improvement of a farm of near six hundred acres, the greatest part of which had been inclosed by the late Earl of Cassillis about sixteen years with a belt of planting, and divided by small strips, which are now giving pretty good shelter to some part of the ground.

The soil is various, but generally light and thin, upon a very hard till, under which is chiefly freestone rock, exposed to the north and west, and, like most hanging ground, full of springs and wet spots. Most of the land was lying as it came out of the hands of several small tenants, except about thirty acres which had been limed, but quite worn out, and in the worst condition of any. There was scarce five acres together in any field in the same condition; three or four acres of old croft in one part, so much outfield in another, and many spots of half an acre, or an acre, which never had a plough in them. In every field the old ridges were lying five or six different ways, some very high and broad, others as narrow, with high gathered head–ridges lying various ways cross the field as the land had been ploughed. The whole farm did not produce hay and corn sufficient for the horses, and almost every necessary for the family was bought, except mutton and lamb. The stock consisted of only as many sheep as supplied the family with these articles, and about twenty–four horses and cows."

"Finding the land in this condition, I could see no possibility of getting it into a proper tilth for grass, or any other crops, but by clean summer fallows. I did not think it prudent to begin my operations by liming upon the surface, as the after ploughings and levelling must have buried a great part of it. I therefore plough first for oats, not expecting much of a crop; but this helps to rot the old surface, and mellow it for summer ploughing; and, as I have sometimes more land under oats than I can get properly fallowed and manured the next year, I am then obliged to take two crops of oats from some part of the land; after which I give it a complete summer's ploughing, four, five, and sometimes six furrows, before I can get it perfectly fine and level; and after getting it clean of stones, and draining all the wet spots, I give it two hundred and forty bushels of lime–shells, and about thirty double cart–loads of compost dung. I then plough it in by ridging up the land as straight as possible, and draw furrows cross the ridges where it is necessary for carrying off the water; these furrows are all cleaned out with a spade to keep the land dry during the winter. In the spring I sow it with barley or bear, and with it grass seeds, from which I take but one crop of hay, and then pasture it; and this is the course I intend to pursue, till I have taken in the whole farm. I now have a hundred and twenty–six acres well laid into grass. My hay crops and pasture are both good; and, as it increases, I add to my stock of cattle, which makes a considerable yearly increase of dung, which enables me every year to take in a greater quantity of ground. I have this winter seventy–six head of horses and black cattle upon corn and fodder. I have these two years past supplied the family with every necessary from the farm. I have every year sold some grain; and have now both cattle and sheep for the market."

"It may be a matter of surprise to you that I have not all this while thought of green crops for the winter feeding of cattle: It is not, however, for want of thought. I know the value of those crops too well to neglect them; but there are many things against the culture of them yet. This coarse kind of ground takes so much time and labour, that the season is always too far spent before I can get it properly dressed and manured. I have, however, this year above twenty acres of cole or rape; but being obliged to send to London for the seed, it was near a month too late; it is nevertheless a tolerable crop, and will afford a good deal of food for my cattle and sheep in the month of March and April, when the land will be in perfect order for barley; and as rapeseed may be sown at least one month later than turnip, and requires no other labour or expence than the seed, I shall make this a substitute for other green crops till a better course can be taken. My chief design at present is only to put the land into a proper condition for a more perfect system of husbandry; but several things are wanting before that can be completely carried on. I have not a proper farm–yard, nor a shed or house for feeding cattle, or for the conveniency of raising near so much dung as might be made; but these things will come in course. Lord Cassillis has an extensive and very commodious plan of offices, which he intends to build soon.[49] His Lordship is now making some improvements here, both in building and planting, besides inclosing many farms at a distance, which must in a few years make an agreeable alteration upon the face of the country."

"My crops, you may imagine, will not be great; but, as they are, I send you the mean product of three years, having threshed but one stack of the fourth, I can go no farther. They are as follows: Oats, seven bushels on an acre; produce, thirty–two bushels. Barley, two bushels and a half; produce, something more than forty. Bear, two bushels and a half; produce, forty–four. Pease, three bushels; produce, only twelve. Wheat, I sowed eighteen bushels upon six acres, part of fallow prepared for barley for crop 1776; the season was so wet I could not get it sown till the end of October, and the hard frost that winter hurt it much; it was very thin upon the ground, and the product only twenty bushels an acre. The small quantity of pease I sow upon land intended for fallow. I do the same with oats. This I do, because it would otherwise interfere with my fallows, barely and grass crops. I always harrow in a little lime with the seed."

"The measures of the above are by the Winchester bushel and the Scotch acre, as is also the lime. My compound middings, which I lay on with lime, consist of farm–yard dung, sea–weed, and earth.[50] I have no stated proportions of each, as the quantity of sea–weed is uncertain, there being a greater quantity thrown out some years than others. I use all I can get, with which I mix up all my dung, and a good quantity of earth. I have tried the sea–weed made into middings by itself, but it does not do so well as when mixed with dung and earth; for this imbibes all the juices which run off in great quantities when thrown into middings by itself; and when mixed with dung and earth, it ferments and rots much faster, and makes a very rich manure."

"I have never made any trial of the weight of my hay crops; but I think I can safely say they have not been less than a hundred and fifty stone upon an acre; the greatest part of last year's crop, I am almost convinced, was near two hundred. The usual quantity of seeds I sow are eight pounds of red clover, six of white, four pounds of ribb-grass, and one bushel of ryegrass. After the hay crop, I pasture it with horses, black cattle, and sheep. I think it an advantage to eat it pretty bare, as it grows thicker and sweeter the next summer. I go regularly over the grass fields every summer, to root out all the docks, thistles, &c. And this is all that I see necessary for the improvement of the pasture at present."

"As to the soil and climate being best adapted for grass or grain, I do not think that the culture of either can be carried on to any degree of perfection separately. The soil is, in general, very proper for turnip and artificial grasses; consequently grain and those crops ought to be cultivated together. And I dare say that you will allow, that any light land farm, under such a culture, will produce considerably more cattle and grain yearly, that it can do so either of them separately. The climate is indeed wet, but the soil in general agrees with it. And as the autumn rains are always succeeded by high winds, the crops do not suffer more by it here than in many other places; and, except about the edges of the moor, the grain is always good."

"I wish I had found this farm in the condition I am endeavouring to put it, as I should in that case have been able to have given you some account of a very different course of husbandry, which might perhaps have done me some credit, and have been more satisfactory to your inquiries. I am not sure (as I have mislaid your letter), if I have answered all your inquiries; if I have not, please to point out the particulars, and I shall do it in another letter."

From Maybole, all along to Ayr, the industrious hand of improved husbandry is visible. Much land is inclosed with ditch and hedge; the quicks, trained with care, make a considerable advance.[51] But I cannot refrain from disapproving of planting crab apple trees among the thorns. The practice is general here; but it will be regretted when out of time to correct the error. Thorns can never succeed in company with trees of a quicker growth; they cannot bear to be overtopped, and never grow strong in that situation. Some miles before I reached Ayr, I found myself in a rich plain of wide extent, greatly improved by means of shell marl—on every side, and in every field, luxuriant crops of corn. Many farmers are conspicuous for good husbandry, where not many years ago there were few or none. John Hall in Achandrain, a tenant of Sir Adam Fergusson's, is one of those.[52] His culture is beyond ordinary. His ridges are made straight, level, and neatly done up; all his crops excellent. Mr Binning of Machrimore is another.[53] I mention these as a sample out of many.

Ayr

Ayr is a sea–port town that makes some figure in trade. Lime is imported from Whitehaven, and lime–stone from Ireland, which, "when burnt, costs about 15d for four bushels. *John Campbell of Wellwood* takes the lead here, both in trade and husbandry.[54] He is a gentleman of spirit, of attention, and of enterprise. The coal–trade carried on by him, both for home sale and for exportation, is very considerable, and circulates much money. He carries 1400 weight in a cart with a single horse, and three of these are managed by a single man. This is a very great saving.

I surveyed Mr Campbell's farm of *Milcraig,* which well deserves to be surveyed, considering what he has made of it from the poor state it was in originally; the soil mean and moorish, carrying short heath and a few dwarf whins; and, over and above, the ground reduced to the most wretched state that bad husbandry could reduce it to.[55] Mr Campbell, however, attempted this beggarly farm on a long lease. He begun with trying to force grass by spreading lime on the surface. It lay for years without producing any; nor was the effect better when ploughed into the ground. Mr Campbell, thus disappointed, examined the state of the lime and of the ground; he found the lime caked and run together, and liker a paste than a manure. The nature of lime, with respect to moisture, is particular. Water dissolves burnt lime into powder, in appearance perfectly dry; but, lay powdered lime in a heap accessible to water, and in time it becomes so hard as to require a pick–ax to separate it. The lime here had been laid on a wet clay soil, which made it run together; and hence Mr Campbell justly concluded, that, to make the lime operate, it was necessary to lay the ground perfectly dry, and then to mix the powdered lime intimately with it. He now summer–fallows two years successively, pulverizing the ground by ploughing, breaking, and harrowing. In this state 800 Winchester bushels of lime are spread on the acre, hot from the kiln, and ploughed in immediately.[56] As soon as dry in the spring, the land gets another furrow, in order to make a still more intimate mixture of the lime with the soil. Two successive crops are taken, both good. He grudges not the expence of Blainsly oats for seed, though the distance is great; but the expence is repaid him in some measure, by selling the produce to his neighbours for feed.[57] To another field he has applied soap–leys with success: And, upon the whole, he has brought this farm into good order.

Sundrum

I proceeded to view the farm of *Mr Hamilton of Sundrum,* a gentleman early initiated in the art of husbandry.[58] He begun with inclosing, &c; but, to avoid repetition, I confine myself to his latest improvements. He holds by the principle, that manure can only effectually operate when mixed with the soil. Lime therefore is only used with summer–fallow, mixed with the soil by reiterated ploughing and harrowing, 600 bushels being given to an acre. He finds the advantage of this practice, in the produce both of corn and grass, which is superior to any of his former ones.

Much of his soil is a thin clay on a till bottom, whence the difficulty of keeping it dry. Mr Hamilton, after repeated experiments, adheres to ridges nine feet broad as the best for that purpose: He alledges, that broader ridges cannot be laid dry, without being thrice gathered, which impoverishes the furrows; that narrower ridges cannot be sufficiently raised by one gathering, and that two gatherings raise them too high.

John Hamilton of Sundrum (1739–1821)

from a portrait in County Buildings, Ayr

Mr Hamilton has converted a moss of 31 acres into a fertile field. The history merits peculiar attention. The bottom is sand, a happy circumstance that suggested the plan of operation. A main drain was opened, cut down to the bed of sand. Small drains were also cut down to the sand, 18 inches wide at top, diminishing gradually to two inches at bottom, and communicate with the main drain. These were in parallel lines, from twenty to forty feet asunder, as the wetness of the moss required. Brushwood was laid in ten inches high from the bottom, and covered with a sod, the rough side undermost; the remainder of the space to the top was filled with the moss thrown out to make the drain. The moss being thus laid dry, various ploughs were used, but none made proper work, except one of Mr Hamilton's contrivance, which was kept steady in the loose soil by two wheels fixed to the end of the beam. Of all the manures tried, soap–leys answer the best; and now to the cropping, after the ground was brought into proper order. Oats was the first crop, and an immense one, no fewer than 80 bushels Winchester measure from an acre. Next turnip seed sowed broadcast, after dung. The turnip three times hoed. The crop was surprising, and the sugar loaf turnip stood the winter the best. They were consumed by cattle at the stall, which, with a little hay and straw daily, produced a considerable profit. As soon as the turnip were exhausted in the spring, two ploughings were given, and the land made up into ridges nine feet broad, for a crop of bear and grass seeds. The bear sold on the foot for £8 every acre. The grass seeds were two bushels ryegrass, 12 pounds white clover, and six pounds ribwort: but a natural tender grass rushed up in such abundance as to supplant every one of the sown grasses, the ribwort only excepted. The crops of hay were weighty; and so dry is the moss at present, as to bear the heaviest cattle while pasturing.

This gentleman spares no cost in draining, which is peculiarly necessary in a wet country and clay soil. The lawn before his house, a clay soil, formerly wet, is made now perfectly dry by capital drains filled with stone, and side drains twenty feet asunder, done up as described above. It is clothed now with a thick sward of the best grasses.

Great attention is paid to the plantations. No tree thrives there if planted so deep as the till bottom; the trees therefore are planted on the surface, and bulked up. Elm is the only tree that does not thrive. Open drains in the planted ground have a good effect.

Gadgirth

This country is happy in its clergy, who are leaders of the people in temporal, as well as spiritual concerns. Many of them are skilful in the improvement of land and, as they have a more immediate commerce with the country people than gentlemen of estates have, they are in the best situation for instructing the tenants in their art. I have occasionally mentioned some of them; and it now falls in my way to mention the Reverend Mr Steel of Gadgirth, who possesses the character of being eminent as a gentleman, a clergyman, and an improver.[59] I have not in all my surveys seen better culture, nor a finer appearance of corn, clover, pasture, hay, turnip, potatoes, both in drills four feet intervals, nicely dressed. I was charmed to see every branch of his husbandry in perfect order. I recommend this practice of husbandry to those in the country who wish to imitate the best example. Plantations of trees and the hedges thrive exceedingly, and the house and offices may be called elegant, and are very commodious. I avoid mentioning particulars, for his own state will be more accurate and instructing, than any I could give, which he most obligingly promised to give me in writing, and I give it to the public in his own words, as a valuable piece of intelligence.

Minutes of Mr Steele's improvements.
"Gadgirth, Dec. 11. 1777."

"I have not been an extensive farmer, but have taken some pains with a large tract of very poor land, whereof I became proprietor in the year 1740. It was quite covered with furze and short heath upon a hard tilly bottom, but easily reduced by frost, summer heat, and repeated ploughings. After having inclosed and divided it with ditch and hedge, in a manner afterwards described, and in such a direction as might best carry off the water that could not pass through the hard bottom, I next hoed out the furze, gathered them in heaps upon the ground, then ploughed up with eight oxen; cross ploughed it, and, with a heavy triangular brake, tore the lumps to pieces, until nothing but the coarse vegetable part remained, which I also added to the heaps of furze, roots turned up by the plough.[60] These I burnt in the first dry weather in the spring; and having twice ploughed the ridges to about six feet broad, I sowed oats in the end of March, and scattered the ashes I had from the burnt heaps, harrowing them in with the grain. I had upwards of seven quarters upon the acre, and upon grinding them had 21 pecks of meal from the quarter."[*]

"I ploughed down the stubble after harvest, gave it a small quantity of dung in the beginning, of March after two ploughings, and sowed it with pease, covering them with a light furrow, from which I had two quarters and a half *per* acre, with a good deal of straw. I ploughed down the stubble, which was left very rough; next spring I ploughed it twice, going deeper at every ploughing, and raised some of the till bottom which was reduced by the seasons, and helped to deepen the soil when incorporated with it. I sowed it again with pease, without additional manure, and had a better crop than the former."

"Having got a good quantity of dung from the pease straw, wherewith I fed my oxen to good advantage, I sowed bear and had a very good crop; but did not lay it down, as I foresaw that the seeds of furze and heath would vegetate again, unless they were, by frequent ploughings, made to spring, in order to their destruction, by after ploughings, which I effected by alternate crops of pease and bear, adding a small quantity of dung to the bear crop, and ploughing three or four times to each crop. I found that the additional ploughings, beyond what are usually given to crops of bear, were equal, at least, to the half of the dung that is commonly applied for raising bear crops. By this course of management, having made the soil quite mellow, and killed the seeds shed upon it in its natural state, I laid it down, after many ploughings, with dung, bear, and grass seeds; I had an excellent crop of bear,

---

[*] *Original footnote:* The English quarter is meant here.

and the two succeeding hay crops were remarkably good.* This was my method with many wild fields in the state above mentioned, which in succession were used in the same way."

"As to the grounds which have been scratched and scourged by the tenants before I came to the possession of it, they were such poor, hungry objects, and so cursed for the sake of their former persecutors, as made me despair of ever rousing them into a state of vigour and fertility; for even resting did them little or no good. The means of enriching them was not easily had, lime being very distant and expensive."

"Ploughing was the chief measure I had recourse to; and having given it a small quantity of dung, after several ploughings, I sowed it with pease, and had a tolerable crop. I turned down the stubble before winter, and gave it one furrow in the spring, which brought it to a proper state for planting potatoes, which I did at four feet distance between the rows, horse–hoed the interstices, and hand–hoed about the plants. I did not give them above a third part of the dung that is usually applied for wheat or barley. The ground is hereby thoroughly fallowed, and the crop has always amounted to above 40 bolls upon the Scots acre; which being sold even at the low price of sixpence *per* peck, weighing equal to four pecks of meal, makes a good return, especially as the weeds are destroyed, the soil pulverised, and made fit for carrying a good crop of wheat with one furrow, without any manure. The potatoes are taken off in the end of September, and the wheat sown immediately. If the land is laid up in ridges through the winter, barley may be sown in the spring without further manure."

"I follow the same plan with turnip, and sow barley or bear in the spring, the turnip being eat off by the middle of March, having given the ground two furrows."

"The method I follow as to kail is much the same. As early as the state of ground will permit, I lay it up in ridges before winter. I sow white pease of all kinds in separate drills, and beans of all kinds in other drills, keeping the kinds separated. This being done with dung in the drills, about the middle of February I plough the inter–spaces several times, as the crops require, until the end of June. I then plant cabbage and kail of all kinds on the sides of the drills, which do no hurt to the crops, and are not hurt by them; and when the pease and beans are taken off, the kail have full room to spread, and their roots to penetrate into the dung in the drills. I have by this method as good crops of each of these as if they were all in separate rows. The kail, though four feet distant in the rows, came to meet in the

---

* *Original footnote*: "I am not clear that the seed of whins can be totally destroyed by ploughing, even in the course of any given number of years, as my own experience teaches me, that whins resume their place after 20 years tillage, and cropping with corn."

beginning of October, and came to a very great size. They are not hurt by the severest frost, except perhaps some of the cabbages; the ground is quite covered by them; and when the garden crops of greens last year were all destroyed by frost, I did not lose one plant."

"Having lime–stone to bring from Ayr in the spring, I sent a great parcel of kail to be sold in the street, and had about £3 Sterling for an acre, besides a great deal I applied to my own use. I feed my milk cows with them in frost, when the turnip cannot be raised."

"After two ploughings in April, I sow barley or bear with very good success. I have tried the red Jamaica yam in the same way, and have upward of a hundred of increase. They are not reckoned so good for eating as the potatoe, but are equally good for cattle of all kinds, and they are all fond of them. I had many of them this season weighing three pounds of 24 ounces each. They grow so strong and thick in the stalks, and took so much earth to support them, as to make it needful to put them at six feet distance in the rows, and two feet in the drill, for the future."

"As to the method of managing ground already improved, I have little to add to what has been written by very good hands, and generally known, however little practised. In applying lime, I find that a small quantity scattered equally on the ploughed surface, and harrowed in with the grain with the last bout, has a much better effect than a great quantity applied in any other way.

"As to the management of grass–fields after they are laid down, I in that, as in everything else, lay aside systems, as they fetter invention, and stop the progress of improvement, which reason, attention, and steadiness only can promote."

"As I have a great deal of coal culm or small coal left above ground from coal pits I have in that field, I burn it in heaps, still adding more as the fire breaks out, until I have a great quantity of ashes that have been burning for several months. In place of dung, I lay these in drills for turnip, putting some of the mellow earth above them before I sow the seed. And here I have the largest and best turnips I ever saw. These ashes, mixed with pigeon dung, bring extremely good onions, garlic, shallot, &c."

"Of Inclosing and Planting"

"My inclosures are most of them made with a ditch about five feet wide. I plant always two rows of thorn, the top of the thorn below thereby filling up the interval betwixt the stems of the two thorns above, and thickens the hedge. I put a crab at about 20 feet distance in the hedge–row, which I inoculated with apples, from which I have the pleasure of blossom, without much fruit. About a foot above the thorns I put in slips of different roses, which do no hurt to the hedge, and are a very cheap ornament, especially on the sides of roads. As I gave every dike a back drain of about a foot wide, I laid the turf or surface taken out of it on the side, to keep up the earth that composed the dike. About a foot and a half from it, I planted a row of well–grown trees, particularly beech, oak, elm, sweet chesnut, which I raised with great balls of their own earth. This not only secured their steadiness, but also their quick growth, as they had a double surface to feed upon. This method I still continue, as trees carefully planted in this way never fail, and make an amazing progress, whereof I have thousands of valid and thriving witnesses. I raise and nurse all my trees, and put them at such distances in the nursery as to be able to raise them with such a quantity of their own earth as not to hurt their fibres in the raising."

"Most of the divisions I have made are done with stripes of planting. Such as extend to the length of an English mile, I have made 150 feet broad between hedge and hedge, planting 50 feet on each side, and leaving 50 feet of a walk in middle. The front lines next the walk are planted with beech and lime, and filled up behind, at an equal distance between the front trees, with laburnum, wild service, wild cornel, &c.[61] I plant the principal trees within the stripes at about twenty feet distance, and fill up the intervals with all kinds of firs, leaving room to the pinaster to grow in its natural luxuriancy, as its leaf keeps a perpetual verdure."[62]

"When I first began to plant, I put in a good deal of birch, but have given that up, except a few of the weeping ones, as the seed of them spreads, and infects the neighbouring grounds; and never came to any account, compared with the firs, which, in 25 years from their being planted, I cut away from oppressing better trees, and sold from one shilling to four shillings *per* tree, at the rate of £50 *per* year from ten acre, and so on through sixty years in rotation. The next clearing must yield much more, as the good trees must be more relieved. The birch, planted the same year, came to small account. I could not draw more than from a penny to a shilling for each tree. They give but little shelter, though they afford a variety when thinly scattered among other trees."

"Others of my division stripes I make narrow or wide according to their length; and proportion the size of my plantations on the highest grounds suitable to the extent of their summits, and follow the circular or oval figure of them with the fence which bounds the plantation; making opens from the centre or not, according to the beauty of the objects that can be seen from them."

"I give the ground several ploughings before planting; which I always do very near the surface, having suffered much in my early practice by putting my trees into pits, reaching the clay or till bottom, where they stood in a bason of water thro' winter, and were thrown out of the ground or chilled by the frost. By following the other method, I have plantations more advanced in fifteen years than by that in thirty."

"I have heard many gentlemen complaining that so much beech is planted, and regretting that oak had not been put in its place, as its bark is of such value, and its timber better. This will appear not to be well founded, if they consider, that beech is commonly, and indeed properly, placed in front lines of walks or opens, and bear dressing to a regular form: The oak will not bear this, and is more irregular in its growth, obstructing the sight of any object that is meant to be seen in the termination of a walk or opening. The beech will grow where oak will not, and that even upon the poorest sand or gravel, and will there advance more in ten years than the oak in forty, to my certain experience. Besides, it is useful for purposes which the other will not answer; and it is found upon trial, that no timber, even plain, acer majus, or sycamore, or elm, makes better pumps of all kinds than beech.[63] The beauty of its bark, leaves, and shape of its head, say much in its favour. The sorbis silvestris, wild service, mountain ash, or roan tree, I have planted in great numbers behind the front trees in the openings of plantations.[64] Their bark is of equal value with that of the oak:[65] its flower and fruit recommend its beauty, and the thrush and blackbird are fond of its berrys. I plant it alternately with the bird–cherry and laburnum, whose flower is beautiful, and its wood not inferior to mahogany both in colour and durability."[66]

"Of all the trees I have planted, the larix is the quickest grower.[67] I have many of them, at thirty years of age, eighteen inches diameter: Time has not yet tried the duration of the timber; but, for the compactness of its wood, its red colour and strength, it excels the fir, which, besides its beauty, should recommend it to be planted in sheltered places for its usefulness. The Virginian, or Occidental platanus, is another very quick grower, and though late in putting out its leaves in the spring, is the last tree that quits with them, and has this peculiarity, that the leaves are never eaten by vermine. The oriental platanus is a very slow grower, and much inferior to the other in this climate."[68]

"I shall only add to what I have said, a few observations as to my management of a piece of natural wood very near my house. It was chiefly occupied with bramble, black thorn, and stumps of old decayed trees, which left no possibility of pasturing cattle in it. I bargained for the trenching of twelve acres of it at £4 per acre, leaving the good trees at proper distances. After having burnt all the rubbish in the spring, I scattered the ashes, and sowed it with Polish oats, from which I had nine quarters per acre.[69] Next year I ploughed it where the growing trees would permit, pointed about the roots of them, and sowed with oats again with grass seeds, and had a most luxuriant crop. The twigs of the howed trees and trashy grass being hereby killed, I had the following two seasons extremely good hay, and since very good pasture. The remaining trees are in a more thriving state than formerly, and the field is very beautiful. It may be of use to observe, that the black thorn, after being trenched out, never springs again. Though broom and furze frequently do, if they are pulled up by the hand while young, and the ground loose, they may be totally banished. The bramble, by constant cutting, will in time be killed, which it will be difficult to do by any other means, as its roots go too deep to be traced in light soil. By repeated pulling off the leaves of any vegetables, their growth will soon cease, as they feed by the leaves as much as by the roots. By many experiments, and strict attention for many years, to the nature and progress of the different kinds of trees that are suited to our climate, I might swell my observations to a great bulk, and add many to what have been hitherto wrote on that subject. But having little time for speculation, I must proceed to practice, and do with all my might what my hand finds to do, as I am coming down while my trees are coming up."

Auchincruive

Before *Mr Oswald's* purchase of *Auchencruive,* many inclosures were made with hedge and ditch, but the improvement of the soil was reserved for him.[70] The fields near his house are tolerably well dressed, the different crops good, wheat excepted; potatoes in drills well done up, and the pasture fields in good order. I am sorry only to observe, that this gentleman has more farms in his own hand than can be well managed, unless he were to make farming his only business, and give up his time to it. I cannot indeed say that I saw any improvement going on so substantial as to bear much additional rent.

His cows and young flock are in good order, and some of them well chosen; which, with a good bull, will mend the breed in this part of the country.

Barskimming

In passing along to Barskimming, I took notice of a mode of fencing new to me. It was a mixture of elm and white thorn. It had been lately plashed; and the shoots from the elm were so much more vigorous than the thorn, as to make it certain that the thorns will be overtopped, oppressed, and destroyed.[71] There is no way I can think of to prevent this mischief but to apply the knife, for preventing the elm from overgrowing the thorn; nor am I certain that this will perfectly answer. Thorns do always best, free of any foreign mixture. Upon higher ground, bare of both grass and thorn, I observed inclosing going on with thorns and crabs in the same row, which will never thrive. It vexed me that industry should be so improperly applied.

Barskimming, situated on the Water of Ayr, is celebrated for its natural beauties; a fine river winding along in various directions, prominent rocks, deep shelving banks covered with natural and planted trees growing vigorously, and here and there a verdant plain highly cultivated and improved.[72] To these Lord Justice Clerk, the proprietor, has added many artificial beauties and ornaments.[73] The bridge over the water near his house is a grand work. The arch is a segment of a circle, 90 feet 3 inches in diameter, and 90 feet high from the surface of the water to the top of the balustrades. His Lordship has enriched the landscape with various plantations, stored with trees both useful and ornamental. He has inclosed and planted all the banks on both sides of the river, extending six miles on the south, and three miles on the north side. These lofty banks, covered with wood, afford a noble shelter, and variety of figure, highly entertaining to those who for pleasure traverse along the excellent roads made for communication along the summits of the rocks, and by easiest descents into the plains, where the river, and impending rocks, all combine to form a grand object of entertainment to the eye.   And Lockerhill, a singularity of nature, is a very remarkable part of this scenery.[74]

There is, besides, a capital work contrived for shelter, but which, at the same time, is highly beautiful.   It is a belt of trees carried two full miles on the highest part of the ground, at a considerable distance from the river.   It is 200 feet broad. Fifty feet are planted on each side, which leaves 100 feet in the middle, and is cut yearly for hay. But its chief purpose is to be a road of communication round the whole, and an entry to many inclosures. It communicates also with a large plantation just making; and it has a further use, and a capital one, which is to occasion a free circulation of fresh air over the whole plantation. How great must be the value of these plantations a century hence! a more secure fund laid up for heirs, than a large sum of money lent on interest.

Upon one side of the house the soil is clay, upon the other it is dry light land, with heath in plenty upon it. To produce fine grass was his Lordship's view in applying to husbandry, wherein he combined the profitable and ornamental. The first thing was to spread lime on the surface, 140 bolls to the acre of the clay land, 100 bolls to the acre of the light.   Note that this boll makes five Winchester bushels. After lying two years on the surface, the ground was broken up for two successive crops of oats. The turnip on the light land; after fallow with dung; and, lastly, barley with grass seeds. The field now under fallow is well managed, and lime upon it ready to be ploughed in, and forming the ridges, either for wheat this year, or barley next year with grass seeds. I must not disguise my opinion, that this way of managing lime, which has been much practised by theoretical farmers, is the result of an exploded opinion, that lime draws nitre from the air. But the experience of the most expert farmers has ascertained a much better way of managing lime, which is to apply it hot after being well pulverised by slaking; and the more pulverised the soil be, so much the better.

Here is a glorious fund for improvement, a lime–stone rock and coal within two miles of it. His Lordship has erected a draw–kiln for burning it; and his tenants are made welcome to burn as much as they please.[75] This is a very proper encouragement to indolent tenants who stand in need of a spur. But his Lordship is too wise not to have the consequences in view. Lime is a two–edged weapon, and can be used as successfully to impoverish the land as to improve it. The large crops it produces at first will prove a violent temptation with low people, who mind only present gain, to continue liming and cropping till they run out the ground, no less to their own hurt when bound by lease, than to that of the landlord. It is necessary to put such men under restrictions against over–liming and over–cropping.

His Lordship's husbandry operations have been directed by Mr Hans from Northumberland, a skilful operator; and his diligence and success have been rewarded by a farm for himself, which is a valuation acquisition for his Lordship by securing to him a good tenant, who will improve his land instead of wasting it; and will also be a good example, to the rest of the tenants.[76]

Shawwood

David McLure of Shawood is singular in his mode of agriculture.[77] He depends much on mixing lime and earth in a compost, turned over and over at least three times, in which state it remains one full year; if longer, the better. This compost is gradually put in the dunghill, and each stratum of dung carried from the stable is covered with a stratum of it, till the whole be finished. From 100 to 120 loads of a small cart is given to the acre; and the servants, in filling the cart, must be attentive to mix the dung and compost well together. This is a work of much labour. Might not the compost and the dung be as well carried to the land separately, and mixed there in spreading? I think better, for the mixing of the dung with the compost is undoubtedly a hindrance to putrefaction. And I further think, that lime ought never to be mixed with dung in a dunghill, because there is no remedy more effectual than lime to prevent putrefaction. Every soldier knows that, after the loss of many lives in a battle, powdered lime is thrown upon the dead bodies to prevent the unwholesome stench when bodies begin to corrupt.

Another singularity is the sowing pease as the first crop on fallow, which hitherto has not answered, though both lime and dung were given. I am not surprised that pease thrive not in ground rendered loose by frequent ploughing. This effect is increased by lime and dung. Beans, I imagine, might have answered, if laid deep, by sowing them under furrow.

Adamhill

I saw another instance of Mr Campbell of Wellwood's knowledge in husbandry, in the farm of Adam Hill, his property.[78] I met him again in this place, and got from himself his method of improving this farm. He begun with inclosing most substantially by hedge and ditch. The ditch is large, and what is taken out of it forms a stout bank behind the quicks, which are properly planted in the choice of the soil, a little back from the edge of the ditch. The soil in many parts is strong, in other parts lighter, where whins grow; but mostly on a till bottom, that holds water, and therefore unfit for turnip, cabbage, or kail. This land was limed several years ago. Mr Campbell does not scruple to lime a second time. After a thorough summer fallow with both lime and dung, he takes wheat, then barley and grass seeds. Where pasture only is intended, the grass seeds 3 bushels ryegrass and 12 pounds white clover; but is of opinion that 20 pounds will answer better. This surely is light cropping. Another method of cropping is to take oats and pease alternately twice or thrice, giving lime or dung to the pease. He finishes with a fallow to prepare for grass seeds.

For potatoes in the lazy bed way, tops of whin are used instead of dung, and the crop is good.[79]

Sometimes clover and ryegrass are sowed upon wheat in May, and rolled. The wheat is laid flat upon the ground, but soon rises, and is not the worse.

For increasing the dunghill, every particle of hay and straw is consumed in the farm; and the court of offices is commodious for winterers.

The calves are not allowed to suck. Each calf is allowed daily four pints of sweet milk, and is fed so the first three months.

He says that sea shells reduced to powder have an immediate effect. Large shells entire are slow in operating, as they fall to powder by very slow degrees. Shells of oysters, of wilks, of muscles, and of cockels, are soon reduced; but there is a small round shell so hard as scarcely ever to be reduced.

Newfield

Greater variety in the practice of agriculture I have not met with than at Newfield; wheat, beans broadcast and in drills, bere, oats, potatoes, turnip, cabbages. It is difficult to say which of these do best, they are all so good, and the culture so well adapted to the different kinds. Of the different sorts of kail, the curled stands the winter best. Mr Campbell, the proprietor, has studied farming, and conversed with many eminent improvers.[80] To follow him accurately through such diversity of operation would indeed be instructive; but, to make way for others, I must confine myself to a general view.

The soil in general is clay, some strong, some less so. Every field has a slope; and the ridges are formed in that direction, so as to leave little moisture that can do harm. He begins with breaking up the strong land from ley; and two crops of oats are taken in succession, not in hopes of a good return, but in order to rot the sward.[81] A thorough summer–fallow succeeds, in order to reduce the surface, and to level the ridges. If this be not sufficiently done in one year, a second year's fallow is not grudged. The surface thus being sufficiently pulverised, lime is spread at the rate of 1000 bushels *per* acre, and carefully mixed with the soil by much harrowing. The ridges are then formed twelve feet broad, which is done by a single gathering. Dung is then given, and turned in with a deeper furrow, which brings up the lime again to the surface. Wheat, bear, vetches, and oats, have been taken in succession; but Mr Campbell prefers the following rotation; wheat, beans in drills three feet asunder, or broadcast where the ground is perfectly clean. As soon as the beans are removed, a ploughing ensues, to prepare again for wheat. If that crop be prevented by a fall of rain, bear is sown next season. In every case, grass seeds go along. As pasture is chiefly intended after wheat, the seeds are twelve pounds white clover, and four bushels natural hay–seed. Where bear is the crop, 18 pounds red clover is sowed on an acre, which is cut for green food, or made into hay; and, after twice ploughing, wheat is sowed, which finishes the rotation, or a crop of oats, if the wheat be prevented by rain. If I might presume to find fault with the practice of this accomplished improver, it would be to observe, that four bushels of beans broadcast, and three in drills, is too little seed; and that six bushels would answer much better. I took the liberty to suggest to Mr Campbell, that his crop, though a good one, was too thin. Beans suffer much where the plants are not so close as to shelter and support one another. Where they grow thin, wind makes a great impression. Neither do I approve of two ploughings after clover for wheat, excepting only in a stiff clay soil.

After a drilled crop with turnip, barley with grass seeds, follow. Where the land is intended for pasture, white clover and hay seed are sowed as above. Where hay or green food is intended, red clover is sowed. Wheat comes next, and oats finish the rotation.

Heavy land is ploughed with three horses in a line, and land more mellow with two, also in a line, to prevent poaching.[82] This makes a driver necessary; but Mr Campbell thinks that he gains by the addition of a driver, supposing him alert enough to quicken the pace of the horses. Every operation depending on activity of servants, will be expeditious in proportion to the activity of the master. This gentleman makes it a rule to be at the head of every thing himself.

He has tried trenching with the spade successfully. A field of water–fat land was every year flooded. It retained moisture, and was long of drying. It was trenched two spade deep; and in trenching, drains were made at the distance of every twelve yards, and filled with faggots, which effectually drained the whole. The first crop was oats, which grew so vigorously as never to ripen. The second crop, bear and grass–seeds, has a promising appearance. A wet meadow was laid dry by open drains. Slack lime spread on the surface improved the quality of the grass, and produced so much white clover as to make the pasture very rich.

This country is obliged to Mr Campbell in many respects, particularly for raising so much wheat, which is here far from being common. He finds great advantage from the bran, by giving it to his horses, two feeds a day, along with green clover, which enables them to go through more work. Cully's lambs and ewes he has in perfection.[83] He acknowledges that they will yield no profit unless on rich pasture. Their wool, which is fit for combing, has increased in length since he got them, which shows the richness of his pasture. One fleece weighs seven pounds Scotch weight, and gives 15 shillings the stone, being 24 pounds English. The price is the higher because he never smears. The wool of six wedders, three years old, sold for 50 shillings, and the four quarters of each weighed in the shamble, 120 pounds English.[84] Mr Campbell told me of a ewe hog belonging to Mr William Anderson, tenant at Craig, that carried 21 pounds wool, English weight; an amazing quantity.

The Lancaster cows at this place are wearing out of request, from their giving little milk. Mr Campbell entertains high notions of Highland cows, as they give excellent milk; and I am of the same opinion. He attempted to improve the Lancaster kind as to their milk, by a cross with the Highland kind. The breed are handsome, and thrive exceedingly; but give very little milk.

Rents in this country are high. I was told of a farm of 140 acres, whereof 20 not arable, let at 27s 6d *per* acre, and another at 25s. This is a proof not only of a rich soil, but that this country is not destitute of enterprising tenants.

Holms

Matthew Hay tenant in *Holms,* belonging to Mr Dalrymple of Nunraw, pays 20s for each of 120 acres, all arable.[85] The soil is light, and kindly to turnip and clover. This tenant's mode of culture exceeds any I have seen in Ayrshire, performed by one who is merely a tenant. His fallow field of 27 acres is clean and in good order. Six hundred and fifty bushels of lime *per* acre were spread on the flat surface, after which it was ploughed, and straight ridges formed ten feet broad. When I surveyed this fallow after it was ridged, Mr Hay was busy in leading dung to it; and, in order that all his servants might be fully occupied, ten carts were employed, each drawn by a single horse, and drove by women, who are dexterous at that employment. This field was intended for wheat; and, in a wet country like Ayrshire, expedition is of great importance. After finishing this laborious work of dunging, nothing remained but to plough it into the ground, and to water–furrow, to be ready for the crop when proper to be sown. I heartily recommend this practice to every farmer in a wet country. Let not the forming ridges be delayed a moment after the ground is fit for it. The dung may be laid on at leisure, and it answers as well on ridges as before. Beans and pease mixed and in broadcast, are intended for next crop, and then barley with grass–seeds. Where shall we find a plan of cropping more beneficial both for landlord and tenant?

One field of 12 acres drew my attention, the crop of bear on it was remarkably good. The history follows. The first operation for improving this field was a thorough fallow of seven ploughings, limed and dunged in the manner above mentioned. Seven bushels of oats, Winchester measure, were sown on the acre, and sold on the foot, each acre for seven pounds five shillings. The second crop was oats, after a single ploughing. And, for the credit of Joseph White the ploughman, I am glad to mention it was finished in eleven days with two horses only in the plough, without a driver. Each acre produced 80 bushels, and sold for £9 10s 0d. Third crop bear, thrice ploughed and dung; seed 44 bushels upon the whole field. Each acre produced 80 bushels, and sold at market for £11. Fourth crop oats, about equal to the former. Fifth turnip with dung, sowed broadcast; four ploughings, and as many harrowings; hand–hoed twice, and some parts oftener. The turnip very good, and consumed on the field by sheep hurdled. The sheep were Highland old wedders, which cost 15 shillings the head in November, and were sold in March for 24 shillings, which returned about six pounds Sterling for each acre. The next crop bear, that which I saw on the ground. Pease thrive well in this farm, and are frequently introduced in the course of cropping. As the soil answers well for grass, Mr Hay sometimes pastures a field five or six years, to make it the more fit for corn.

Upon a very light gravelly soil, that bears but a mean sort of grass, and is filled with broom, when it lies any time, Mr Hay takes alternate crops of turnip and bear, which have answered well. Another field, a little better as to the soil, carries turnip, bear, and clover in rotation. Dung is given to both fields when in turnip.

His chain–plough is good; but, as there is no perfection in man, I regret the small cart he uses, which will not hold a load sufficient for half a horse. A good stout horse will draw much more than double of what his carts contain.

Mr Cully's sheep have found their way to this farm; and, as Mr Hay reforms in every article, these sheep are in high repute; in evidence of which, he got 30 shillings for lambs, intended for a breed. Last June he refused 25 shillings for year olds offered by butchers for the market. The fleece weighed 8 pounds English, sold at 15 shillings *per* stone. No attempt hitherto of a cross breed has been made. A second or third blood from Cully's kind, with the best of this country, would improve the breed greatly. As the general run of cows and steers is here but indifferent, Mr Hay is attempting an improvement by a mixture with the Holderness kind.

I finish with a neat house and offices. The landlord contributed £160 10s 0d. Mr Hay added £400 on a lease no longer than 30 years.

Collellan

Major Dunlop of Collan has got his field into good grass, and what was formerly outfield is now in good order.[86] Lime is his chief manure, which he always lays on the sward to lie at least a year before breaking up. I forbear going into particulars, which differ little from what have been described frequently above. I shall only mention one article that is new, which is manuring the land with horn shavings, procured from Ireland at the rate of 13 pence *per* barrel, 80 to 100 on an acre. This is a considerable expence, at least £4 6s 8d to the acre. But the major perseveres, and finds his account in it. He has a curious observation, that animals fed with pease or bean straw afford richer dung than even with hay. If this hold, it affords an additional motive for frequent crops of beans and pease.

Wool has engaged the Major's attention several years. He got a breed of sheep from England with long wool, which, upon his dry and kindly pasture, improved in quality, and is now sold at 24 shillings *per* stone, 24 pounds English. The Kilmarnock manufacturers are fond of it. The Major has got a full blooded ram of Bakewell's kind, not so fine a wool as his own.[87] I wish he does not impair his own wool by the cross breed.

Kilmarnock

Labourers and servants are not scarce, though many are drawn from husbandry to the town of Kilmarnock for manufactures. The wages of a hind are five pounds Sterling *per* year, a house and a yard, six and a half bolls oat meal, and a cow maintained. The wages of a day–labourer from tenpence to a shilling, which is higher than in many other parts of Scotland.

Husbandry and manufactures are sister arts, that should go hand in hand, and ought never to separate. They are not, however, altogether free of rivalship more than real sisters are. A manufacture, the younger sister, draws indeed, in its progress, hands from husbandry the eldest; but then it may be doubted whether the younger sister, after it becomes stationary, does not pay its debt by returning hands to the other. Whether Kilmarnock has arrived that length, is a proper subject of inquiry.

The woollen manufactures, carried on to a considerable height in this town, create a constant demand for wool, which cannot be supplied but from a distance. Can the gentlemen in that neighbourhood undertake anything more patriotic than to improve the breed of their sheep, which at the same time is the best plan for raising their rents? Only let them keep their sheep at a distance from hedges, unless they procure the heavy Lincolnshire breed, which are used to inclosures, and easily kept in. Upon rich grass, which that country will plentifully produce by good culture, I doubt not but that such sheep will thrive well. Mr Clerk of Holme has inclosed with hedge and ditch; and his thorns, by careful training, make good appearance.[88] I observed a flock of fine sheep, a mixture of Cully and Bakewell with the natives. The spirit for this species of improvement I hope will spread so as fully to supply the Kilmarnock market, equally for their own benefit and that of the town. But the activity and spirit for trade of this people is not confined to the manufacture of wool into various articles, and that to a very great extent; but several other branches of home manufacture they carry on extensively; and, in the article of shoes made of Scotch tanned leather, I am credibly informed of one house in Kilmarnock exporting not less than £12,000 Sterling worth in each of the two last years; and it is now a melancholy truth, that the trade is lost since parliament granted to Ireland the liberty of exporting shoes, as they pay no excise duty on leather.

Grougar

The estate of *Grougar,* the property of Mr *Colebrook,* is of a rich soil.[89] Seventeen hundred and thirty–three acres arable are let for £1300 Sterling, about 15 shillings *per* acre.

Galston

In passing by *Galston,* I observed the industry of the women. They build the hay into tramp ricks: they load the cart from the rick, and drive it to the stack, and, as mentioned above, they assist in driving dung to the land. But here men servants are not plenty.

Rosemount

The inclosures of Mr *Fullarton* of *Rosemount* with ditch and hedge engaged my attention, being done in a better manner than most in that country; a large ditch opened, the thorns properly planted back from the edge of the ditch, with the best of the soil about the roots, the rest of what is taken out of the ditch thrown backward to form the bank.[90] Quicks so planted cannot fail to prosper.

Milrig

Bruce Campbell of *Hillas,* at Milrigg, is an active gentleman farmer.[91] His inclosing is almost finished. Lime is his chief article for improvement, from 600 to 700 bushels of Winchester measure to the acre. After three corn crops, it is laid down with grass seed for two crops of hay and four years pasture. Then, without scruple, a second liming, 400 or 500 bushels to the acre. By repeated trials, he finds it advantageous that the lime lie two or three years on the surface before ploughing. He takes two crops of oats. Seven bushels produce 56. Next crop pease and beans, after a single furrow; five bushels produce 30. The fourth crop oats; then, after a clean fallow with a compost of earth, lime, and dung, bear is sowed with grass–seeds, ten pounds red clover, four pounds white, and three bushels ryegrass. Four bushels bear produce 50. A better method would have been to have rotted the dung well in the dunghill, and to have carried it directly to the land, without mixing it in a compost, which prevents it rotting. Better also to have spared one bushel of ryegrass, and to have added four pounds white clover. What is mentioned above was done on outfield. With regard to infield, I shall only mention as an instance of his management, that he sold a crop of wheat on the foot for £13 *per* acre. Mr Campbell has reclaimed 25 acres of moss from a swamp, which could not sustain the lightest horse or cow upon the surface from sinking. The whole was let for 50 shillings. He drained it precisely as mentioned above to have been done by Mr Hamilton of Sundrum; and the surface soon became so dry as to be paired and burnt, and to carry a plough with horses.[92] Oats, the first crop, stand now on the ground, a very rich crop. I suggested rapeseeds as proper for such ground.

Many have got into the practice of purchasing hay–seed from England, gathered in hay–lofts. This gentleman, among others, made the trial, but found the crop much inferior to that from sown grasses. It cannot be otherwise, considering that there is no choice in such seed, but all must be taken, good, bad, and indifferent; besides, it is generally the weakest of the kind; and as the English always heat and sweat their hay, the seed is frequently spoiled so much, that it doth not vegetate.

Twenty years ago Mr Campbell procured fine sheep from Elwingfoot, well made, and carrying fine clothing wool.[93] Of late he thought of improving his flock by a ram from Bakewell and one from Cully. The success answered his expectation; the figure and size were improved, and the wool now became long and fit for combing. Bakewell's offspring had a fleece weighing from 6 to 7 pounds; Cully's offspring from 8 to 9 pounds. The fleece of the rams reached 14 pounds. The pasture is not fine, but in great abundance; the inclosure large, well fenced, and low lying. A ram bred at Newfield was put to a parcel of country ewes, which cost Mr Campbell 5s 6d *per* head, and the lambs were sold to a butcher for 9s. But the pasture here must come in for a share of the profit; for the ewes were sold to a butcher, before the middle of August, for 9s.

Loudoun

The *Earl* of *Loudon* keeps 1500 acres in his own hand.[94] The soil, in general, leans to clay, and is naturally good. The greater part is susceptible of much improvement, especially that where there is a mixture of gravel. But it is not without its defects; a till bottom, moss in several parts, and many spouty wet spots. His Lordship spares no pains to put this land in order, nor drains to make it dry. Some of it was so wet and spungy as to require flat stones at the bottom, to prevent the brush–wood from sinking into the moss. When the land is made dry, and a little manure given it, it sends up many plants of natural grass, which soon convert the surface into a sward. His Lordship has seconded the propensity of nature, by aiming chiefly at grass.

One large field opened from ley got 1000 bushels of lime *per* acre, not less than 165 bolls Linlithgow wheat measure, the one half being laid on the grass, the other half on the red land. The crop was oats, an immense quantity of straw, but little corn, which points out an over–dose of lime. The second crop was six bushels beans, mixed with three of pease, *per* acre; product 30. Third crop turnip and cabbage drilled with dung in the rows, which were three feet wide, horse and hand–hoed completely. This crop, which was a great one, was eat by sheep on a dry grass field, and horned cattle in the house, which yielded each acre about £5 10s 0d, including the grass they eat before they were put up. The sheep were stock, and not fattened; but their value was much heightened. Upon one furrow after the turnip, barley was sowed, five bushels *per* acre. The apology for this thick sowing was the multitude of crows invited here by many old trees; the product 80 bushels *per* acre, a very great one. With the barley were sowed twelve pounds red clover and two bushels ryegrass intended for the hay crop, with the addition of white and yellow clover with a view to pasture. I saw the second growth of clover in this field, and none could be better. My admiration is, how such a quantity of corn and grass could stand together: Sown grasses are commonly smothered with a much less quantity of corn. It was remarked, that that part of the field which was ploughed before liming, gave the best first crop, but was inferior to the other part where the lime was laid on the sward in the subsequent crops. I was led into a very large field of old grass filled with rich plants of grass for fattening; white clover, ribwort, the wild fitch, feather grass. There were in this field many horned beasts for fattening, but understocked, with a view to plenty of food in the winter; for they get no other food, unless the ground be covered with snow, which seldom happens here. By this method the very finest of beef is at hand all the year round, and I presume the wholesomest. Cows got from Lorn make a capital figure in this inclosure.[95] They are finely shaped, with a smooth horn, but rough hair, which last are signs of their thriving.

I admired the crops of turnip, potatoes, Aberdeen red cabbage, all in horse–hoeing husbandry. The last is thought to stand the winter best. Potatoes are in high esteem for feeding cattle when frost prevents access to turnip, and wetness prevents access to cabbage. They beside make a variety, of which cattle are fond, as much as men. I saw tares in perfection cut green to feed horses in the house in summer.[96]

Oxen are employed in the plough and wain, without horses. Mr Skelly, the Earl's overseer, is fond of them, though yoked very disadvantageously in the old way; but he has it in view to yoke them like horses with collars and traces. Straw is their only food till January, from which time they get a little hay in the morning. In this estate the encouragement is great for improving. What farms have been undertaken by his Lordship are let for 18s *per* acre, sometimes to tenants who held them before at six shillings, without making anything of them. So poor and spiritless are the tenants of this estate, as to have no ability for improvements, nor will, if they had ability. Yet coal and lime are at hand, and draw–kilns erected for burning; and the Earl has procured an undertaker, who furnishes lime–shells at a penny *per* bushel. This certainly will answer; but it seems that the lime is not yet come.

Here are many old inclosures, mostly fenced with thorn–hedges. In several of them crabs are used instead of thorns, which do not make a good fence; in others they are mixed. In defence of this method, it was urged that the crabs kept down the weeds. Nothing is more common that to find a reason for a thing that has been done without reason. Why should thorns be planted at all, till the ground be perfectly cleaned?

Upon every hill or hillock, for miles round, trees are planted, which afford shelter and prospect, and in time great profit. Ornamental trees are scattered here and there, and many orchards made that afford plenty of cyder. I have been diffuse upon the improvements of this place, because I think the description of it may be a spur to other proprietors.

One word more on sheep; for no article escapes his Lordship that can benefit the country. Mr Bakewell's kind are here, and also Mr Cully's, to which the preference is given. One ram bred from Cully's he lamb and ewe is preferable to any I ever saw. This evinces a rich pasture, and a climate not unfavourable to that kind of sheep. I examined the flock attentively, and singled out a kind of sheep that pleased me more than the rest. These, said my conductor, are the offspring between a ram of Bakewell's and ewes that have been long in this country at Orangefield, that have wool short and fine, which sells at 14 shillings *per* stone.[97] The wool of the offspring is longer and fit for combing, and is sold at 15 shillings *per* stone. Each fleece weighs between ten and twelve pounds English. They lamb in January, and every lamb, at an average, sells for 18 shillings. They are hardy, and will thrive every where in the low parts of Ayrshire.

My road to Glasgow led me into a part of Ayrshire, naked of improvement, tho' the soil is good, and lime and coal in plenty.[98] But no patriot has appeared to rouse the people from their torpid state. This part of the country gives no advantageous impression of the proprietors.

In general, the soil of this country is good, and improveable to a height scarcely at present to be imagined. Limestone, sea shells, and shell marl, can be imported at a moderate expence, sea weed on the coast, and freestone for inclosing. Above all, there is coal in plenty, the great promoter of population in a cold country. The climate is the only obstruction to struggle with, much more rain falling in the west of Britain that in the east. In a gravelly or sandy soil, this would be no great inconvenience; activity and watchfulness will prevent, in a great measure, the bad effects of superfluous moisture. But Ayrshire is a clay soil, which consorts not well with a wet climate; and yet the tenants in Ayrshire, proceeding in the track of their forefathers, adhere to the plough, without having any notion of grass but what is barely sufficient for their labouring cattle. And, by the same bias, grain is their only food. But, if Ayrshire be unfriendly to corn, it is in a high degree friendly to grass. And, to make it perhaps the richest county in Scotland, two things only are necessary; first, to dress their grounds high, and next, to enlarge their kitchen gardens, and to make the produce of their gardens the chief part of their nourishment. The gentlemen–farmers are going with zeal into that plan; and the tenants will in time follow.

What I have given above is but a specimen of the improvements going on in this county. My time would not permit me to go through it with the attention and accuracy that would have been my wish. I have seen little, in particular, of the district of Cunningham, where I am informed improvements go on successfully, as much so as in any other part of the county. I may perhaps be allowed time to bring this district also under my survey.

Second Survey in the Shire of AYR, 1778

Formerly I thought it sufficient to give information to my employers; I now find it necessary to give satisfaction to enterprising farmers, gentlemen, and others, some of whom have complained of having been overlooked. This I hold to be an excellent symptom; and accordingly I found good husbandry spreading every where, and not a few valuable improvements, of which the following report is humbly submitted to the Honourable Board.

Newmilns

I entered this country in the road to *Newmills,* a pleasant vale; but there was little appearance of industry till I reached the Earl of Loudon's estate, mentioned in my last report. I have only to add, that oxen are constantly employed in the plough, harrow, and wain, and give full satisfaction in every particular. Lime answers extraordinarily; the crops it produces are great. The half breed of sheep, formerly mentioned, are further proved to be preferable to those of full blood.

Cessnock

Mr *Wallace,* a merchant in Glasgow, purchased the estate of *Cessnock* some years ago.[99] He begins well with his improvements in husbandry. Lime is his chief manure, of which 100 bolls are allowed for an acre, frequently 140. It is laid on old ley, to lie there two or three years before the land be taken up for corn. This practice prevails in Ayrshire; and many eminent improvers there reckon it better to lie four or five years. It is my opinion, that, by liming on the sward, the improvement of the grass may equal the money laid out in purchasing the lime. I cannot, however, agree to this practice. Lime exposed to the weather many years recovers, by degrees, the air that was expelled out of it by burning, and in time returns to its original estate of limestone, and is consequently unfit for being a manure. But this is not all. Lime spread upon grass, however carefully, has no chance of being so intimately mixed with the soil as when laid upon earth well pulverised by ploughing and harrowing. But still we must acknowledge, that lime operates powerfully when applied as mentioned above, and ploughed the second year of its being on the sward for crops of corn; and yet it is my firm opinion, that the great effect of lime depends on that intimate mixture.

The old timber trees at Cessnock are delightful and of high value. Twenty guineas were refused for one elm. Scotland was once covered with trees, which were rooted out with the same keenness that at present is done in America, till not a tree was left in any place where the plough had access. After a long interval, the inconvenience was felt; and gentlemen, for the sake of shelter, planted trees near their dwellings, to the west especially, and south–west. It is but of late that we have begun to plant for the sake of beauty or profit, or sheltering inclosures. Hence it is that old trees are not to be met with any where in the low country of Scotland, unless close to gentlemen's houses.

Galston

Near to *Galston,* on the side of the road leading to Kilmarnock, I spied a fallow field. It is now the 10th of August, and in lies in the cross furrow, having not yet got the third ploughing. The operator must be either indolent or ignorant. It hurts me to find such neglect in a county remarkable for good husbandry.

Ballochmyle

At *Ballochmile* I saw very extensive improvements carried on by Sir John Whitefoord.[100] He is happy in his overseer Mr Bruce, whose knowledge in farming is great, his practice considerable, and his success corresponds.[101] Happy would it be to the farmers in that neighbourhood, where they wise enough to avail themselves of the example of Mr Bruce, who has had the best opportunities of improvements, and in him is added, to a long experience in the practice of husbandry, an extensive knowledge of botany, and of the other branches of natural history. I should be guilty of injustice to him and to the public, if I suppressed the information I received from him, contained in the following letter.[102]

"Ballochmile, Oct. 20. 1780."

"Sir, I was favoured with your's of the 7th September. I had heard of your being in Ayrshire, and was sorry I had not the pleasure of seeing you here, as it might have been in my power, in the course of conversation, to have given a more full and satisfactory answer to your queries than can be expected in a letter."

"It will give me real pleasure if the information I now send shall be found of any use in forwarding the laudable endeavours of the Honourable Commissioners for the annexed estates to improve husbandry in Scotland. In carrying on their spirited and patriotic plans, it is the duty of every intelligent farmer, who wishes well to his country, to contribute his assistance."

"In the few following particulars, I confine my views chiefly to this part of the country, for four or five miles round where I live, wherein I shall give a short state of the husbandry and practice of the best sort of common farmers, with an example or two of their method of culture, stock, &c. Then I shall beg leave to mention a few of the most interesting parts of my own short practice in this country; and, if I have time, shall offer a few remarks upon the husbandry of Ayrshire, and propose some amendments."

"Ballochmile, and that part of the country which lies in its neighbourhood, are situate upon high rising grounds, about twelve miles distant from the sea. The soil in most places is a strong heavy loam inclining to a reddish clay."

"As the climate is rainy, and the land clay, and having early frosts in autumn, the practice of corn husbandry is attended with many difficulties, which would require all the industry and attention of the most active to surmount."

"The country in the track I speak of, is all under tillage, and a great part of it inclosed with ditch and hedge. Many of the fences are badly executed, but the greatest part are shamefully neglected afterwards."

"Lime as a manure has, within these few years, come into very general use amongst the tenants, and is here in very great plenty, and in some places of a good quality; the price of shell–lime from ninepence to one shilling *per* boll of five Winchester bushels. The roads every where are excellent, and kept in good repair."

"Farms in general are small, from £5 to £30 *per annum,* some few rise to £70, and perhaps a rare instance to £100; the average may be from £15 to £35. Leases are in general of nineteen years, all paid in money. In the present state of this county, the difference between old and new leases is not very great, unless considerable improvements have been made by the landlord. One third, or one half advance, is good; to double is rare, and that with building, inclosing, &c."

"The lands in general are in bad culture, hardly any thing sown except oats, which the soil is peculiarly adapted to. Some bear or big, hardly any barley, a few pease, no wheat or summer fallow.[103] Turnip or cabbage are not known, except in gardens. The worst construction of the old Scotch plough, drawn by four horses, is in general use, without any sort of reason, the land being all in tillage long ago, might be ploughed to great advantage with the small Whittinghame plough, and might be used in most places by two horses without a driver."[104]

"Their ridges are very high and crooked, and, in the country way, are left to rest poor, and without any grass–seeds, so that the country must to strangers exhibit a very dismal spectacle."

"The breed of horses are universally good, and kept in excellent order. Many Irish horses are imported; and the country people are almost all jobbers in that way, and very sharp at taking advantages where they can."

"In the present waste of the grounds, their black cattle are but small, and very few are bred. Their milk–cows, at calving–time, run at an average about four pounds a piece; and, since inclosing came to be so universally practised, gentlemen have found it necessary to exclude sheep almost wholly."

"They all lime upon the sward, from four to eight year old leys. Many of the tenants burn their own lime, and lay on at the rate of from fifty to an hundred bolls to an acre.* Some take four crops of oats, and so let it rest; others only three crops; and some few, who do still better, take two crops of oats, and give a thin dunging; then take bear, and so rest."

"N.B.–If some hay–seed and white clover were here added, it would be sensible; but I am sorry 1 cannot find this to be the case."

---

* *Original footnote:* In this paper the Scotch acre is always to be understood. In measures, the Winchester bushel, and in weights the Trone stone of 24 averdupoise pounds, unless the contrary be expressed.

"Their practice upon their infield or croft land is, to break up their four year old leys with a slight liming, or with their dung. They take two crops of oats, then bear, and so rest, without grass–seeds."

"Few in this neighbourhood begin to plough till February. Some are now beginning to break up their leys throughout winter; others say it is bad for the lands, and washes. Their horses being quite idle throughout the winter, are now in great spirit; and, except feeding an hour in the middle of the day, plough from morn till night without intermission, and will do rather better than an acre a day. They generally plough with four horses, some with three. It is rare to see two horses without a driver."

"It is amazing that draught oxen are entirely unknown, except in one or two instances, and these only by gentlemen."

"Every farmer manufactures his own crop into meal, and in general his bear into malt, and afterwards disposes of them about the country to his best advantage. There are no corn markets in this country. I might likewise mention, that, in the present state of this country, every farmer keeps a superior flock of milk cows, much above what might be expected. This may proceed from a peculiar turn which prevails for the dairy; which practice is good, if made consistent with rearing calves and breeding; likewise feeding fat; but these must all give way to the dairy."

"The profit of a cow from 40 to 50s say £2 5s 0d; and if 30s be deducted for winter and summer feeding, the trifling profit of 15s would perhaps strike them with surprise, and this the more, as the profit of hogs is altogether unknown."

"These, in general, are the outlines of our oeconomy here."

"I shall now beg leave to lay before you a particular state of one or two of the better sort of country farms, which will likewise serve to illustrate what has hither–to been advanced."

"Some particulars of a corn farm, partly inclosed. Take as follows:
150 acres in all.
100 grass.
50 arable.
£65 rent, together with cess and road–money to be added.
6 horses.
1 colt.
12 milk cows.
18 young cattle.
30 sheep.
No piggs.
2 men, wages, £6.
2 boys, wages, 20s.

1 maid, wages, £3.

Wages in harvest with victuals:

Men, 21s.

Women, 17s.

"Six year old leys limed on the sward, at 80 bolls per acre. Take three crops of oats; sow six bushels, and get upon an average 48."

"For croft land rested four years, dung or lime upon the sward, and take, 1st, oats; sow 7 bushels, and get 55; 2d, bear; sow 3½ bushels, and get 48; 3d, oats, sow and reap as above; 4th, pease; sow 3 bushels and get sometimes 24."

"Have this year one acre of sown grass; plough generally with 4 horses and a driver."

"Another, all inclosed, upon a strong clay. Take as follows:

80 acres in all.

48 grass.

32 arable.

£24 rent.

15 acres oats.

12 bear with grass–seeds.

2 pease.

3 meadows.

4 horses.

No oxen.

2 colts.

10 milk cows.

6 young beasts.

1 fat beast, 2 pet sheep.

Sometimes keeps a brood sow and finds it profitable.

Wages in harvest:

Men 21s.

Women 17s.

2 servants, 1st £7 10s 0d.

2nd ditto, £6.

1 maid £3.

1 boy £1.

"Generally plough with four horses with a driver; sometimes with two, but rare. Lime six years old leys, and break them up first February thereafter, at the rate of 100 bolls *per* acre, and crop as follows: 1st, oats; sow 6 bushels, and get 48. 2d, oats; sow the same, and get sometimes better. 3d, beans and pease; sow 3 bushels, and get 16. 4th, bear with 3 earths; sow 4 bushels, and get 36. The bear crop sown with 10 lb clover, and 2 bushels ryegrass."

"Have tried wheat after pease and beans, and had a good crop; and thinks, after fallow, he might get good crops of wheat."

"That I may not be too tedious in multiplying examples, I shall only beg leave to produce one other important instance of a Northumberland farmer settled some years ago in this part of the country, whose oeconomy and stock, I believe, may be depended upon."[105]

"Farm generally a strong clay, and partly a black muir earth, all inclosed, and very well sheltered with belts and clumps of planting."

165 acres in all.

110 grass.

55 arable.

£148 rent.

8 horses.

1 colt.

15 milk cows.

1 bull.

4 young beasts.

6 fattening beasts.

4 men, wages, £7.

1 boy, £2.

2 maids, £3.

Implements:

2 ploughs, Whittinghame kind.

1 break.

1 roller.

4 double carts, &c.

"Eight year old leys broke up with, 1st, oats without lime; sow 7 bushels, and get 48. 2d, Pease, and part oats; pease are uncertain. 3d, oats. 4th, summer fallow with lime and dung. Lime at the rate of 70 bolls *per* acre, and sow. 5th, Wheat, and part bear and barley, all sown out with grass–seeds, 10 lb red, 5 lb white clover, and 3 bushels ryegrass *per* acre."

"Take two crops of hay, and pasture six years."

"Use [blank] horses in a plough, and do [blank] acre a day."

"Sow 3 bushels wheat, and get 48. Bear, sow 3 bushels and get 48. Pease, an uncertain crop."

"Have tried turnip, and find wheat more sure."

"Have tried flax, but think it scourges the land, and deprives the cattle of fodder, and, upon the whole, is not profitable here."

"Have sown 6 acres lint in one season, 8 pecks *per* acre of seed, and saved over the field 24 pecks *per* acre. Stacks the lint over winter, and steeps it in the first of May, after threshing and cleaning, &c., the seed."

"The kind of lime used here is a caulmstone burnt; it operates but slowly; but its good effects appear beyond the fourth year."[106]

"I shall draw no conclusions from the above particulars, nor state a comparison between the practice of the ordinary farmers of this country, and those of the last mentioned gentleman."

"In justice, however, to several noblemen and gentlemen here, I must observe, that they have exerted themselves to introduce better practices, and a more spirited mode of agriculture; particularly the Right Honourable the Lord Justice Clerk, for having not only brought the above mentioned intelligent farmer into the country, but likewise an ingenious plough and cart–wright, bred at one of the best manufactories in the north of England, whose carts and ploughs are spreading in the country very fast."[107]

"By an attention and an expence so praiseworthy as this, and the example followed by others, local prejudices would in time wear out, and this beautiful country become one of the richest in Scotland."

"Having already transgressed the ordinary bounds of a letter, I shall now take the liberty, in a more cursory manner, to mention only a few of the most capital parts of my own practice."

"The parks of Ballochmile are all well inclosed, between 200 and 300 acres, generally a strong wet heavy clay, naturally producing rush, spret, carex, &c. all these encouraged by the wetness of the soil and bad husbandry."[108]

"In narrating matters of husbandry, I think it equally unfair to suppress the unsuccessful parts, as it would be to add favourable circumstances to those already prosperous. Therefore I shall relate measures just as they stand."

"After premising that, in this place, we use the small Whittinghame plough, and likewise the Norfolk wheeled plough, two horses and no driver, take a six inch furrow, and seldom plough so much as half an acre *per* day."

"In 1775, a ten acre field that had carried a crop of oats the preceding year, the ridges high and crooked, gave it a winter furrow. Spring 1776 was favourable; reduced and cleared the field with other four ploughings; gave it a very slight liming, 30 bolls shells *per* acre; threw it into 15 feet drills, which were slightly dunged, and sown with turnip; 7th to the 15th June finished, and it turned out a very good close middling crop, nearly equal to the best I ever had in Berwickshire."

"The season was favourable, and they were regularly horse and hand–hoed. The autumn rains soon deluged the field, and rotted many, notwithstanding they were used early in the season, being drove off to a grass field for feeding Highland stots and sheep, a bad way of using them in this high wet country."[109]

"In spring 1777, as soon as the season would permit, cross ploughed, and laid the field in nine feet ridges, and latter end of April sowed it with barley."

"Red clover 15, and white 10 lb to the acre, with three bushels ryegrass. The wet clay parts had little or no barley, but a most extraordinary crop of grass. The dry found parts of the field brought a luxuriant crop, both of barley and grass."

"In 1778, a rich crop of hay is cut from the field this year; but find, upon the clay parts, the clover much gone off, and in the furrow rushes appearing in plenty; but these only in the clay parts."

"Last year, 1777, was a wet summer here. I had another ten acre field, all strong clay, in preparation for turnip and cabbages, after a crop of oats the preceding year. I only got forward with two acres of turnip and one acre of cabbage in good time, and was stopt by the rains, when I turned my thoughts to a crop of wheat upon the remainder of the field, which was substantially dunged and limed at the rate of 120 bolls *per* acre. Threw the whole into nine feet ridges; sowed three bushels *per* acre by the 12th August, and part 1st September, and the last upon the 21st October. The early sown a very fine crop, at least 48 bushels *per* acre, but was not ready for cutting till the 15th September; the middle sowing was equally good. The latest sown was not ripe till three weeks after, and a very thin crop, and not well filled."

"The turnip part of the field a mere shadow, little larger than goose eggs, not above eight ton *per* acre; and the cabbage very trifling."

"The above field was sown out with grass–seeds amongst the wheat, and part amongst barley. Those amongst barley the best, but both very good. The barley very bad, occasioned by a wet season after sowing."

"From the above, and some other trials I have made here, I have every reason to conclude that, in a dry favourable season, with due preparation, very good crops of turnip may be got. Wheat likewise may be a sure crop, if properly attended to in preparing the ground, and sowing about the beginning of September at farthest. Grass–seeds, if they are not sown with too niggardly a hand, will pay the industrious cultivator most liberally. Pease, I know from experience likewise, in a dry season, to be a profitable crop after oats upon limed land. Spring tares I have tried two years unsuccessfully, both times owing to late sowing."

"From the above short, but I hope, true state of agriculture in this part of Ayrshire, many inferences might be drawn, and deductions made, which I shall leave to the ingenious who may peruse this paper, and only for a moment longer beg your indulgence, while I observe, that,

"Since lime is plenty, and marl to be found in some places; the soil in general extremely good, and the lands all well situated for culture; the people strong, numerous, and healthy; a good breed of horses, and in general the land cheap rented; this seems to be a spot where, in some future period, great things may be expected in agriculture."

"Let gentlemen, by a spirited example, point out to their tenants and others, the most improved practice in husbandry, and persevere in them for a few years, and, in different places of the country, introduce a good south country farmer, whose example might perhaps operate more than the landlord's. And, finally, if I might venture to give a hint or two, of so much consequence to the public as the improvement of a country, I should, with the utmost diffidence, propose, first, to better their practices in tillage; secondly, to have fine fields of grass pointed out as their principal object. And,

"As the stubborn soil here is but too just an emblem of the prejudices and strong prepossessions of the inhabitants, it would therefore be adviseable not to push them on to the very extremity of good culture all at once. Their eyes will open by degrees. At first, to introduce summer fallow as a means only of reducing these unprofitable high ridges. Totally to level and alter them all at once, is beyond the ability of very many, and against the inclination of almost all."

"Therefore, in cropping the infield or croft land, let that be done in its present state and form, previous to any sort of manuring. Lay it into three or four breaks, according to the size of the farm, and so reduce the ridges by four or five cleavings and cross ploughings; manure and sow the ridges thus reduced without alteration. The outfield land in the same manner. Time will shew them the propriety, and even necessity, of totally levelling and straighting both."

"Once persuade them to summer fallow, and reduce the high ridges, (one third waste at present), great crops of oats will be gained, off all their worst outfield lands, with lime only; and, upon their croft and better sort of field lands, they may, with half liming and dung added, have good crops of wheat, beans and pease, barley and oats in course."

"But if, in this wet cold climate, the ultimate views of gentlemen farmers could be brought to terminate in luxuriant crops of grass, which is very attainable, and to raise their rents partly by rearing young cattle and horses for sale, feeding fat both sheep and black cattle, together with the dairy, would in the end, and with far less expence, make them both rich and happy; in place of annually ploughing this heavy wet soil, to the great oppression of men and horses, who, after all their labour, are not able, in many instances, to gain twice the seed they sow. This is no less a true, than a melancholy fact."

"As a further and necessary improvement, let me recommend to every well–wisher of his country, not as a local, but as it would be a national advantage, that the use of oxen for the draught by all possible means be brought into practice in a country and soil so highly proper. This topic has already been so fully discussed by many able pens, that I pass it over; and shall conclude this tiresome letter with pointing out to the industrious and well–meaning farmer, a course or two of corn cropping in his prosecution of the above plan, previous to the sowing off his land with grass–seeds."

"Upon his worst outfield land take, first year, summer fallow, and reduce the high ridges, and with the last furrow lay them gently round, ploughing in your lime before harvest, 100 bolls *per* acre at least. Second year, oats. Third year, pease and beans. Fourth year, bear, after two furrows; and if a little dung is given, the better, and sow off the bear land with 12 pound of white clover and four bushels ryegrass or hay–seed, to be pastured six years at least."

"Secondly, upon the croft and better sort of outfield ground, having, previous to manuring, taken what crops of oats, &c. are requisite from the part intended for summer fallow, the ridges being reduced by two cleavings and two crops ploughings; let the last ploughings be a gathering furrow; immediately before which, spread your lime at the rate of 50 or 60 bolls *per* acre; likewise the dung; let both of which be equally spread, and the ridge gathered up with a light furrow. First year, wheat, sow three bushels red Kent by the first of September at latest. Second year, bear or barley. Third year, pease and beans. Fourth year, bear or barley with grass seeds; 12 lb red, and 8 lb white clover, *per* acre, with three bushels ryegrass; to be cut for hay two years, and pasture at least six."

"But, if wheat is not relished as a crop in course, then the following may do: First year, fallow with lime and dung as above. Second year, barley or bear. Third year, oats. Fourth year, pease and beans. Fifth year, bear, and sow with grass–seeds as above."

"But it is unnecessary to multiply courses, as these, and every other thing relative to the best practical husbandry, are treated at full length in the Gentleman Farmer, lately published.[110] If the Honourable Author of that valuable little work were pleased, in a future edition, to make its title page less formidable to poor country farmers, it would be more generally read, and I know of no book so proper to be consulted."

"Therefore, at present, shall only beg leave, that, in case of a more enterprising farmer, he might promise himself superior advantages in the following course: First, summer fallow, level and straight the old ridges, and manure as above. Second year, wheat over the whole fallow. Third year, a miscellaneous crop of part potatoes, part turnip, cabbages, drilled beans, and part tares for a green feed in place of clover: these all well horse and hand hoed, except the tares, will make an excellent preparation for, fourth year, barley, to be sown out with grass–seeds as above directed, which may be safely mown two years for hay, and afterwards pastured from four to six years or more."

"From the small knowledge I have of the genius and manner of the country people here, I have ventured the above as my present opinion of the manner by which improvements in husbandry might be introduced, so as to become more general in this part of the county."

"In giving the above directions, many years practice and experience have been my guide; truth, and a regard to usefulness, my motive; both which have been more in my eye that any regard to trifling embellishments. It will make me infinitely more happy, if the above, or any part of it, shall answer the intention of the Honourable Commissioners, or coincide with the views you had in writing me."

"That the plans of that honourable and patriotic body may be attended with the highest success, is the earnest wish of, &c."

Sorn Castle

At *Sorn Castle,*[111] the very venerable and highly respected Countess of Loudon resides, now in the 98th or 99th year of her age, as I am informed, and yet as entire in memory and judgement as in the prime of life.[112] Her Ladyship has graced this country in many respects; but I am confined to her husbandry improvements. Fifty years ago, when this lady took up her residence at Sorn Castle, not a tree was to be seen, a scrubby wood excepted; and now the finest oaks and other barren trees are striving, as it were, which shall rise the highest. The plantations are extensive, and all trained in the best order, every thing directed by the Countess herself. The soil of her farm is far from being kindly; yet, by skill and perseverance, she has brought it into high order; not greater verdure can be seen any where. In a word, her farm graces the county of Ayr, and might grace the richest counties of Britain.

I had the honour, which will not readily go out of mind, to be introduced to this noble personage. She entered familiarly into a conversation with me, and surprised me with her knowledge in husbandry; discoursed on the qualities of various grasses; inquired into the method of raising potatoes from the apple; and expressed uncommon zeal for husbandry improvements. There perhaps does not exist in the world such another woman.

The wages of labourers are high in this county, from 12d to 14d *per* day, occasioned by the great drain of men for the army. This bears hard upon agriculture; but the public must be served; and, in the mean time, children are growing up to fill the vacancy.

In my former survey of this county, I had occasion to mention some ministers, exemplary not only for good living, but for good husbandry. I am glad to add to the list Mr *Connal,* minister of *Sorn,* who adheres to the following rotation.[113] Lime is at hand, fivepence *per* boll. He lays 100 bolls *per* acre on the sward, to be opened up for oats, pease, oats. Grass–seeds are sown with the last crop, barley sometimes instead of oats; and six years pasture finishes the rotation. This method cannot fail to produce good crops; and, where lime is to be had, it may suit even the humblest tenant. I only doubt a little whether lime be not here too often repeated. Judicious farmers agree in theory, if not in practice, that, in the culture of a field, change of seed is not more necessary than a change of manure.

Auchinleck

As I advanced toward *Cumnock*, I passed through a farm of *Lord Auchinleck's* estate, mostly a thin moorish ground.[114] I cast my eye upon a very good crop of oats after fallow and lime. The ridges were raised so high as to leave the furrows bare of soil, and without a single stalk of corn. I do not pretend to condemn this method in a wet climate. High ridges preserve dry four–fifths of the surface; and better abandon the remaining fifth, than that the whole should be wet. But I find speculative improvers, and now and then a practical farmer, doubting whether very narrow ridges, well gathered up, and carefully water furrowed, would not answer better. I am confirmed, by long experience, that no ridge should be narrower than 15 feet.

Lord Auchinleck is a most assiduous planter, and equally careful of his trees, though indeed in that wet climate, they require little else but to be fenced from the cattle. His closures are extensive, and his own farm is mostly in grass. Upon his broad walks lined with trees and consequently well sheltered, hay is commonly taken. But the culture of corn, a most laborious operation in a wet climate, and clay soil, is generally left to tenants; nor, in such circumstances, can success be expected but by a close and punctual attendance. His Lordship, therefore, in my opinion, judges rightly in confining himself to the propagation of trees, which require not close attendance. His office as judge in the two sovereign courts of session and justiciary, occupies at least two thirds of his time; and every time he returns home he has the satisfaction to find his plantations in a prosperous state, and every tree growing more and more beautiful.

Cumnock

Cumnock is a neat clean village, pleasantly situated near the water of Lugar. Here is carried on a small branch of the woollen manufacture. A few shoemakers in that town make for exportation about 3000 pair of shoes, a considerable article for private tradesmen.

Dumfries House

Dumfries–house was built by the late Earl, who, at the same time, inclosed and planted much.[115] In particular, 35 acres, not far from the house, were planted with oaks, which are now beautiful and grow luxuriously. This has encouraged the present Earl to continue the plantations in belts round his inclosures, and clumps on every height, which embellish the country at present, and in time will be very profitable. The land which the Earl has in his own hand extends to 1200 acres, including pleasure ground.

Lady Dumfries is the best assistant that ever blessed a man who delights in improvements. She is the very soul of husbandry and manufactures in that part of the country. She zealously patronises the woollen manufacture at Cumnock, and the linen manufacture all around, giving premiums to promote each. In that view, her Ladyship has excellent crops of flax on her Lord's farm, so extensive, as more than once to have gained premiums given by the trustees for manufactures.[116]

More particularly with respect to agriculture, it is amazing what skill her Ladyship has acquired in a few years, which she puts in execution, by relieving her Lord almost wholly of the trouble of attendance. She is a substitute that leaves nothing undone. A field of level ground, frequently under water by the over-flowing of the river Lugar, was rendered no better than a bog. Much draining was necessary, and parallel drains were opened; the distance more or less, according to the degree of wetness, and all filled with brushwood. The ground being made now dry, a part proper for turnip was dunged in the rows, well hoed, and a very good crop raised. The rest was fallowed for corn, straight ridges made 10 feet broad, and 50 bolls shell lime given to each acre. One half was sown with wheat: I saw the crop, which was uncommonly good. The barley on the remaining part was good. The whole was sown with grass–seeds, never again to be opened.

His Lordship's mode of liming is 100 bolls of shells *per* acre, laid in summer on the grass sward, to lie three years before opening with the plough. The reason given is, that this limestone, being full of sand, falls not into powder in less time; and that even then it is not fine, but of a gritty substance; which, however, operated mightily upon the clay soils in this country. The quantity of sand in that limestone is indeed a good reason for the great quantity that is given of it, but not for allowing it to lie so long on the surface, subject to the inconveniency of returning it in some degree to its original state of raw lime–stone.[*] Nor can I have any doubt, but that plenty of water will make it fall instantly into as fine a powder as it will do by being long exposed to moisture from the air. There is a lime–stone quarry in that neighbourhood, which, when slaked, falls into a very fine powder, and is reckoned better upon light soil; undoubtedly, because light soil would rather be hurt by sand, which is little inferior to lime itself for clay soil.

Turnip, cabbage, potatoes, pease and beans, are raised on the light soils, all in drills, which make a fine preparation for barley and grass–seeds. The clay land is summer fallowed for wheat. On land opened from ley, oats is the first crop. If it be very stiff, a second crop of oats is taken, in order that the sward may be thoroughly rotted. The next crop is drilled beans with dung.

There being a great demand for grass in this country, no sooner is an inclosure ready to be let, than there are many bidders for it. The Earl's only

---

[*] *Original footnote:* See p.235 and vol. II p.142. [The passage he refers to on page 235 is on page 46 of this book].

difficulty is to confine them within bounds; and he seldom accepts of rent more than 20s *per* acre. This demand for grass is not confined to graziers. The neighbouring tenants stand as much in need of it. Rather than lay down any part of the farm in grass, they are willing to pay the rent mentioned; though it is seldom that their farms in corn return above three after one. Strange, that men should be so blinded by custom against the light of common sense. But Ayrshire need not surprise us. The low country of Berwickshire was in the same stile 30 years ago; and East Lothian too, wherein a few obstinate tenants still persist to persevere even to this day.

Red clover does not succeed here. In a rainy climate, the ground is seldom dry in winter; and upon ground when wet frost makes a great impression. Hence it is that red clover does not thrive here. It is too tender either for frost or for moisture. Ryegrass never fails, and is sown in plenty. I recommend white clover and ribwort as hardy plants, than can endure a severe season.

Sheep of any kind and weight will thrive here, as the pasture is fine, and the grass rises in plenty. The Earl, therefore, is thinking of improving his sheep by cross breeding. At the same time, his object is not the highest priced sheep, but what will suit the general staple of the country. The last thing I have to observe is that the water of Lugar is a troublesome neighbour, by laying waste many fine spots on its banks. The Earl, by a laborious work, has widened its bed, raised banks with an easy slope, and sowed natural grass to bring a sward on the bank, that may preserve it from being pitted by the water in a flood.

Drongan

My course carried me over a high land, exposed to stormy weather, a poor thin moorish soil, and little done to make it better. In the midst of a scene so dispiriting, I was refreshed by the inclosures of *Drongan*.[117] Perceiving the hand of an intelligent and bold enterpriser, I learned that all was done by Mr *Smith*, whom I unluckily missed.[118] The soil cannot be boasted of; but this gentleman, by a singular effort of genius and application, has made a wonderful change. I begged of him in a letter to favour the public with particulars. His answer follows.

"Drongan, Sept. 3. 1778."

"I had some time ago the pleasure of receiving a letter from you. I am sorry I was so unlucky as to be from home when you intended me the honour of a visit; but, had you examined more particularly the state of my farm, and manner of cultivation, you perhaps would not have had so high an opinion of my knowledge as a farmer as you seem to have at present; though it is certain my farm wears a very different aspect now from what it did in the year 1770, being the first season I had it in my power to get any quantity of manure brought to it worth mentioning, on account of having no made road till that time; and as, since that time, I have had too many things to do to attend to the *minutiæ* of farming, my methods of cultivation have been very simple. In the first place, most parts of my land were outfield long rested, at least fifty years, and covered with a mixture of short flowering heath, bent, and spret, in which case my way has been to lay on the sward at the rate of 160 bolls of five Winchester bushels of lime in powder *per* acre; sometimes more, but never less on old rested land. But though I say at the rate of five Winchester bushels of powdered lime to the boll, I do not mean that my lime is reduced to powder before it is laid on the land, as I always lay it on so soon as I can from the kiln, and it is often too much slaked by the weather before I can get it led out. This lime I sometimes let ly on the ground three years before ploughing, as I am convinced the longer it lies the better, and never plough any that has not lain at least one year, unless some small part of a field that has not been finished for want of lime, or some other circumstance.* From that land I commonly take three crops of oats running, the last always the best; and I always find the crops best where the lime has lain longest on the sward, but most remarkably so in the first crop. After the three crops of oats, I generally sow gray pease; but, as the soil and climate are unfriendly, it is frequently late in the season before I can sow them. I seldom have many pease, but always a great quantity of straw, equal to any crops of hay I can expect; so that I do not think myself disappointed. After the pease I sow bear, with about eighteen bolls of red and white clover, and three bushels of ryegrass to the acre, giving betwixt forty and fifty double carts of dung to the acre, and two or three ploughings, as the season, and my other operations, will permit. This is my method when the land is well swarded, and the ridges narrow, and of course, flat or even, so that I can easily make them straight, without burying any of the manure; but, when the ridges are broad and raised in the middle, or any bare places that have been made so by the storms, I then summer fallow the land, if I may use that expression, before I lay on the lime; but it almost as properly deserves the name of winter fallow; for I give it the first ploughing in the winter, when, on account of the stiffness of the sward and bent roots, I am obliged to take as large a furrow as four oxen or four good horses can draw, to make it turn over."

"In that state it lies all next summer, the following winter and spring; for, was it to be attempted sooner, which I have done, no plough, with ever so sharp irons, could cut it to plough it cross; as ploughing it in the same direction as first time, before the furrows get time to grow together, would make every one of them turn over whole. In the course of the second summer I get it reduced to a proper tilth, the ridges made straight, and the lime, about 100 or 120 bolls an acre, laid on, and sometimes spread and ploughed in, and sometimes I do not get the whole lime

---

* *Original footnote:* See p.235 and vol. II p.142. [The passage he refers to on page 235 is on page 46 of this book].

on until I get it on in time of frost, and then use it in the same way as when limed on the sward; which method I rather prefer, though my experience is not such as enables me to decide which is best. I have sometimes tried pease first after fallowing and liming, but never had a crop equal to the seed and labour, allowing only for one ploughing; and some gentlemen not far from me have tried it with no better success. I also sometimes give dung for the pease, after three crops of oats, and make bear afterwards without any, which answers tolerably well; but I think it best to give the dung to the bear."

"You will be perhaps be surprised that I mention nothing of wheat, beans, and barley. I have tried them all; and though I have had tolerable crops, yet I am convinced, that, in such a climate as Ayrshire, oats, gray pease, and bear are more profitable. I should have mentioned that my land is generally a strong red clay. Besides lime, I have laid on, at different times, 300 or 400 tons of sea–shells, at the rate of 15 tons to the acre; but I think lime answers fully as well; and on one field of twenty–one acres, after treating it as already mentioned with the bear crops, I harrowed in 860 barrels of horn shavings, and had a very indifferent crop. What effect they may have when the field is broke up again, I know not; but I shall not be in haste to purchase any more of them. Thus far I have sat down, in a very bad forenoon, to answer your letter; and if you have the occasion to be in this country, will be happy to see you at this house, I am, &c."

"P.S. Since the year 1769 I have laid on near 100,000 bolls of lime."

Rosemount

I wish, for the sake of good thorn–hedges, that every man who deals in such fences would take a lesson from Mr *Fullerton* of *Rosemount*.[119] None have I seen go before them. They would have been still better, had the sheers been used more sparingly, and had they been trained as directed in the Gentleman Farmer. In the former report [see page 42], I have described the plan of his ditch, and way of laying the quicks. I call this gentleman a spirited improver; for, in the space of ten years, he has erected a large elegant house, and made a garden suitable to it. He has completed an extensive shrubbery, humouring the course of a winding rivulet, done in the highest taste. And, to sum up all, no fewer than 500 acres, never before cultivated, are divided into neat inclosures, pastured by sheep and horned cattle. It was my misfortune to miss Mr Fullerton; but my loss was supplied by his Lady, who received me with great affability.[120] It appears that she has not been an inattentive spectator to her husband's operations; for she gave me the following account of them.

A summer fallow was always laid hold of to level and straight the ridges. Those that were made 15 feet broad have answered best, both in grass and corn. A ridge of 10 or 12 feet broad cannot be cleaved at every ploughing; and if gathered twice, it is raised too high for the breadth, which also renders it difficult to be properly ploughed for any crop or crops to follow. Nor can it be turned conveniently into alternate crown and furrow. Though the ridges were not altered till the ground was made perfectly level, yet the old crowns and furrows appear distinctly to this day. To lower and straight ridges in a rainy climate, like that of Ayrshire, must be a very difficult operation.

This farm being but a few miles from the sea, about 350 cart–load of sea–weed is annually brought to the farm, and mixed with dung from the stable and byre. It is in the month of August spread upon the fallow, and turned with the plough at seed–furrowing. Wheat is sown the first week of September. If barley be the crop, it is not sown till the last week of April. Grass–seeds are sown with the barley, not with the wheat; three bushels ryegrass, four pounds red clover, eight of white, two pounds of yellow clover, and as much ryegrass.[121] I need not add, that they are intended for pasture, not for hay.

Turnip is raised from sea–weed. Cabbage is tried this year upon sea–weed, and also upon compost. The sea–weed appears to do best.

I add as a voucher of Mr Fullerton's skill, that every crop I viewed was good and early; wheat, barley, oats, bear, pease, and beans.

Clay soil, on a till bottom, in a rainy climate especially, should never be laid down flat in grass. I grasp at every opportunity to condemn this pernicious practice, though few gentlemen give proper attention to it. Mr Fullerton has fallen into this error, through the motive, I presume, of having a fine lawn around his house. The land is rendered so wet by every fall of rain, as to be poached with cattle, and rushes have got up and are spreading.[122] Nay, on several spots, water lies on the surface. This quick–sighted improver, sensible of his error, intends to open the field again, to form the ridges of a proper breadth, and to be so raised as to send every drop of water to the furrows; and these being kept open, will preserve the land perfectly dry.

As the state of the farm is now such as to afford rich pasture in every field, Mr Fullerton intends to pasture with sheep, in order to prevent poaching; and he is intent upon having the very best kind. But here I must make a caveat against breeding from ewes that carry short wool, and a ram that carries long. They should never be mixed; because the wool of their progeny must be of a mongrel kind, unfit either for the combing or clothing manufacture.

Orangefield

I lost much instruction by the absence of Mr *Dalrymple* of *Orangefield*.[123] He has a notable subject to work on; and, from every appearance in the great plain where his house stands, not a ridge is left unimproved, a great part of it being covered with grass.[124] His fences are good, and his hay, standing in ricks on the field, appeared a great crop. He draws, as I am informed, 40s *per* acre for many of his pasture fields.

Fullarton

I bent my course to the house of *Fullerton;* the proprietor was also absent. This estate is justly famed for the real improvements done by the late Mr Fullerton.[125] I say nothing of the present proprietor. His character, as a man of science and talents for business, is well known, both in Britain and France.[126] As this gentleman showed an early inclination for improvements in husbandry, and as he has many hundred acres to work on that were not overtaken by his father, there is little doubt, if he had settled at home, that his superior talents would have enabled him to make a figure among the most celebrated improvers in Britain. But ambition led him to a higher sphere of action, and has deprived this country of a youth who, in all appearance, would have been one of its chief ornaments for agriculture; but I hope not for ever. After he has served his country, and gratified his ambition, it is hoped he will return to private life, and follow out with ardour the embellishment of his fields and improvement of his fortune.

Irvine

If the erecting a large church, with a genteel steeple, be evidence of a thriving town, *Irvine* is in that state.[127] It flourishes by the coal trade; and any staple article of commerce never fails to promote other articles. The coal trade at Newcastle is what brought on many other branches of commerce, which have made that town rich and populous.

Ashgrove

Ashgrove is not a delightful situation, nor much planting on it, the soil a cold wet clay, and part of it a sort of morass; yet Provost Bowman of Glasgow, an eminent merchant, made the purchase from the motive of its being the place of his nativity; but, being a stranger both to the theory and practice of husbandry, he proceeded with wary steps.[128] His first attempt was on a piece of wet obstinate land, of about two acres, intended for a garden. By hollow drains covered above, he has dried the ground effectually. Sand, sea–shells, and lime, were laid on in abundance, which were intimately mixed with the soil by frequent ploughing and harrowing. And now the ground is improved to a garden mould, so effectually, that nowhere are there to be seen better crops of whatever is proper for the kitchen. This encouraging trial made Mr Bowman extend his view to the fields, where he has followed out the same operations which proved so successful in his kitchen garden. To the articles above mentioned, he now adds moss; and I have not seen any compost manure more effectual, especially on grass. He has lately made a purchase of the estate of Mongreenan, a more grateful soil than that of Ashgrove, and partly improved by the former proprietor.[129] But, when Mr Bowman shall finish the improvement of his first purchase by laying down the whole in good pasture grass, he will find it an easier task to complete the improvements of his new purchase.

Blair

Major Blair of Blair lays himself out to give comfort and assistance to all the lower ranks of people in his neighbourhood, particularly to his own tenants.[130] He never takes advantage of a hard lease, where the tenant does not thrive upon it, but sets him free to follow some other course. He benefits by this humane practice, having always the best tenants to choose upon; not only so, but he takes pains, by giving good example, to lead on his tenants, by degrees, to do better and better. The farms are inclosed at his expence, and the hedges carefully reared. He is active in the making good roads, and contributes liberally out of his own pocket for carrying on the work. He gives encouraging leases on moderate terms, 9 shillings or so per acre is the rent; and he lays down a plan of husbandry, no less profitable to his tenants than to the estate. They are taken bound to lay 800 bushels, Winchester measure, of powdered lime on each acre of what has been in grass five or six years before, sufficient for a soil between light and heavy, wet and dry. The first crop is oats, always good. The next pease, beans, or bear, to which dung is given. The third and last is oats with grass–seeds. This rotation is imperfect for want of summer fallow, or drilled crops of broad–leaved plants. But the Major will not be long of introducing these. He leads the example himself; and I observe several tenants near the village of Dalry that are imitating him; none to such perfection as the Reverend Mr Fullerton.[131] Would the tenants of his parish take a lesson from him, they might profit greatly, both in their spiritual and temporal affairs.

On this extensive estate, many plantations have been raised, and are still raising by our improver. Clumps he approves of most; and every hillock is covered with trees. These additions to the old planting give shelter and ornament to this corner, naturally bleak and bare, and in no time will be of great value. There are no fewer than 4000 acres inclosed.

Major Blair has been so much engaged in the improvements mentioned, as scarce to have thought of improving the breed of his sheep, though he has a very large flock. Salving, in particular, goes on in the old absurd way, much tar and little grease. This improvement is a reserve for the Major; and when he sets his heart upon it, he will find it turn to great account.

Towns of Cunninghame

This is a populous country; and the villages of Dalry, Beath, Kilwinning, are in a flourishing state, chiefly by the manufacture of silk gauze, and other branches they have got from Paisley. Irvine and Saltcoats, seaport–towns, are increasing in numbers, as well as Greenock. Every production of land finds a ready market; and though, by improvements in husbandry, more corn and flesh meat are produced than formerly, yet not near sufficient for the increase of population. How encouraging is this to farmers? He must be a drone indeed, who is not roused by it. With respect to the village of Dalry, I was informed, that, 30 years ago, it was a rarity if a single cow was killed in a whole year; and it was thought great luxury to purchase part of it. Now, above a hundred beeves are consumed yearly. But this great increase of manufactures is attended with one inconveniency, namely, high wages of labourers, a shilling a–day in summer, and tenpence in winter. But let not the farmer be discouraged. Even in the growing state of manufactures, he profits more by a ready market at home, than he loses by high wages. And when manufactures become stationary, as soon or late they must do in every country, they furnish more labourers to husbandry than they took from it in their low estate. Husbandry and manufactures are intimate friends, and, in the main, sort well together.

I passed along the vale of *Rayholm,* an extensive field of rich soil. The grain upon it is indeed good; but as for grass, I never saw worse. The tenants take crops of white corn till the land will bear no more; and then abandon it, to find a clothing for itself, thistles commonly, and other unprofitable weeds. It vexed me to see Lord Glasgow's fine land in such wretched order.

There are many small feuers hereabout, dozing away their time without doing anything. Give an industrious man a feu, and he will work wonders. Give an idle man a feu, and it will encourage him to be still more idle. And such as men are, such will be their children.

The shire of Ayr is perhaps of all in Scotland the most difficult to be subdued, a rainy climate, a stubborn soil on a till bottom. Yet there are found, as mentioned in my reports, men of spirit and enterprise, who have attempted this arduous work, and been thoroughly successful in the only plan that is fit for this country, little corn, but much grass, with a proportion of roots and broad–leaved plants. These are the true patriots, that have no occasion for a mask; and they will prove a great blessing to their country, if they can engage others to follow their example. Interest will do much, if people can once be brought to understand it; and, if the plan mentioned become universal in Ayrshire, it will turn from the lowest state of husbandry to the highest.

Colonel William Fullarton of Fullarton:

A biographical note

by Rob Close

Unlike Wight, William Fullarton, whose account of the agriculture of Ayrshire follows, was a native of Ayrshire. Consequently, this short biographical note is included. As will be observed, Fullarton's life and career deserve fuller and more analytical investigation than the scope of this volume allows.[132]

William Fullarton was born on the 12th January 1754. He was the only son, and heir, to William Fullarton of Fullarton and his wife, Barbara Blair, a daughter of William Blair of Blair, who had been married in 1751. Fullarton is a small and compact estate on the Ayrshire littoral, largely within the parish of Dundonald, stretching southwards from Irvine, and including most of what we now know as Troon. This estate had been in the hands of the Fullartons since at least the 13th Century. Colonel[133] Fullarton's father had done much to improve the estate: "This gentleman devoted much time to the study of agriculture and rural science, and greatly improved and embellished the paternal estate. In 1745 he built the present house of Fullarton,[134] in which, and its accompaniments, he showed a just taste, by the simplicity and unity of the design. Gardening and botany he also cultivated with much assiduity and success – particularly the latter, of which he was a devoted admirer."[135]

William Fullarton died in 1759, when his son was only 5 years old. During his minority, management of the estate would have been in the hands of his mother,[136] and of his Tutors.[137] Little is known of the development of the estate at this period. It is perhaps worth commenting that the stretch of coast here, especially at Troon, was a noted landing–place for smugglers during the late 18th Century. In choosing Troon, the 'free–traders' may have been swayed by the lack of a resident landlord. Certainly, the customs officials at Ayr noted that "Mrs Fullerton [sic], life rentrix of that place, will not let any house to an officer of the revenue, because she receives exhorbitant rents for them, from smugglers,"[138] and that when customs officials went to Fullarton in April 1767, hoping to get the keys to the Temple which William Fullarton had built at Troon, they found that Mrs Fullarton was in London and that "none of her staff knew, or were prepared to admit to knowing, where the keys were kept."[139]

During this period, Colonel Fullarton was receiving an education in Edinburgh, where he spent some time at the University. In 1769 he was placed under the tutelage of Patrick Brydone, and with him travelled on the continent. He was with Brydone when he visited Sicily and Malta in 1770, the journey which furnished Brydone with the material for his book *Tour through Sicily and Malta* (1773), which was one of the first books in English on those islands. Brydone noted of the tour that "Fullarton has been urging me to it with all that ardour which a new prospect of acquiring knowledge ever inspires [in] him."[140] He acceded to the estate in 1775, when he became 21.

Colonel Fullarton's initial intention was to join the diplomatic service, and he spent some months as principal secretary to Lord Stormont's embassy in Paris, returning to Britain in 1778 when Britain and France went to war.[141] In 1779 he was elected to parliament as the member for the borough of Plympton, in Devon. The following year he did not seek re–election, as in the meantime a proposal of his had been accepted by the Government. He, and his close friend Thomas Humberstone Mackenzie, Earl of Seaforth,[142] would each raise, equip, at their own expense, and command a regiment: the intention being that these regiments would be shipped to Mexico to await and capture the Spanish fleet based at Acapulco. The regiments were raised, and on 29th May 1780 Fullarton was gazetted as lieutenant–colonel–commandant of the 98th Regiment. However, in the meantime, Britain had gone to war against Holland, and the destination of the regiments was changed, firstly to the Cape of Good Hope, and then to India, where they were to take part in the Second War against Haidar Ali.[143]

This is not the place to discuss in depth Fullarton's career in India.[144] His success in India enhanced his reputation considerably. In June 1782, he had been made a colonel in the army of the East Indies, and his diplomatic skills were used to considerable effect in settling the perpetual niggling which had characterised relationships between the armies of the crown and the East India Company. On the field of battle, he captured the city of Palghat, and the important fortress of Coimbatore. Paterson records that his "campaigns and operations ... were attended with a rapidity and brilliancy of success altogether unknown in that distempered and enervating climate."[145] The capture of Coimbatore followed the breaking of the terms of the surrender of Mangalore by Ali's successor, Tipu Sultan: however at this juncture the "pusillanimous" [*DNB*] government of Madras ordered a halt to all fighting, and settled peace terms with Tipu. On his return to Britain, Fullarton published in 1787 "A View of the English Interests in India", and other works which outlined his operations in the sub–continent.

Now, Colonel Fullarton devoted himself to his Ayrshire estate. It was during this period that his account of the agriculture of Ayrshire (which follows) was published, and he also produced a pioneering work on the advantages of pasture land. These books "have been highly esteemed both for the accuracy of the scientific observations and the classical elegance of the composition."[146] He also interested himself in industrial improvement, and in 1792 obtained a patent for an improved method of crushing iron ore and smelting cast and wrought iron.[147] His efforts in these various fields were rewarded by fellowships of the Royal Society, and the Royal Society of Edinburgh.

In 1792 Colonel Fullarton married Marianne Mackay, the eldest daughter of the 5th Lord Reay.[148] Her mother was Elizabeth Fairlie, cousin of another noted Ayrshire improver, Alexander Fairlie of Fairlie. Colonel Fullarton continued to interest himself in military issues, and raised two further regiments: the 23rd, or Fullarton's, Dragoons in 1794, and the 101st, or Fullarton's Foot, in 1800, but both were reduced after the Peace of Amiens in 1802.

Colonel Fullarton resumed his parliamentary career, but seems never to have achieved much in that arena. Parliament was, perhaps, too much a talking–shop for a man of his talents. Nonetheless he served as M.P. for Haddington Burghs from 1787 to 1790, as M.P. for Horsham from 1793 to 1796, and finally for Ayrshire from 1796 until April 1803. Boswell and Fullarton were in opposing camps, politically, and Boswell fought to prevent Fullarton securing the nomination for Ayrshire in 1790. Nonetheless, when the minister of Auchinleck, John Dun, died in October 1792, Colonel Fullarton wrote to Boswell that "many trumpeters of the Gospel will be anxious to labour in that vineyard, and of course you will be assailed with solicitations as various as the forms and colours of the caxons* which adorn the pastors of our church, from the ample, bushy cauliflower or dalmahoy to the smug, meagre curl closely adhering to the lank withers of the more rigid votaries of John Knox, predestination and original sin."[149]

During the years that he served in parliament, Fullarton was often away from Ayrshire, and management of the estate devolved upon an overseer. From about 1793, this was Alexander Bruce, who had a tenancy of Fullarton's farm of Darley.[150] However, this relationship did not prove a happy one for Fullarton. Returning to Scotland in 1795 he was dissatisfied with Bruce's conduct, but was unwilling "to take the harsh measure of turning him out of his employment", because he had a large family, but by 1799 he had discovered that Bruce was embezzling money, and he was dismissed.[151]

In April 1803, Fullarton was appointed as one of three commissioners for the government of Trinidad. His fellow commissioners were Samuel Hood, a Captain in the Royal Navy, and Lieutenant–Colonel Thomas Picton, who had governed the island since it had fallen to the British in 1797. However the two men had incompatible approaches to colonial government: it is suggested that Fullarton "conceived an instant dislike of Picton's overbearing military demeanour" [DNB]. What began as a general debate on the nature of the government of newly–conquered territories rapidly degenerated into a bitter personal conflict between Fullarton and Picton. In February 1806 Picton was tried for torturing a Spanish girl, Luisa Calderon, in the hope of extorting a confession

---

* wigs

from her. He was found guilty, but appealed for a second trial, at which he was ultimately acquitted. However, before this new trial was concluded, Colonel Fullarton had died, of inflammation of the lungs, at Gordon's Hotel, London, on the 13th February 1808.

Unfortunately for Fullarton, in this last chapter of his varied career, he was cast as the villain, 'the persecutor of Picton', and the fame he gained in India, and the work he did on agricultural improvement overshadowed by this final bitter quarrel. His death was, however, "deeply regretted by a numerous circle of friends, to whom he was much endeared, not more from his highly cultivated mind, in almost every branch of literature and science, than from his amiable dispositions, and condescending affability; which latter quality entwined him round the hearts and affections of his vassals and tenantry."[152]

In 1805, as the controversy over Trinidad raged about him, Colonel Fullarton had sold the family estate in Ayrshire to William Henry Bentinck, Marquis of Titchfield (who succeeded as 4th Duke of Portland in 1809), so greatly facilitating Bentinck's plan for a line of railway linking his coal–rich Kilmarnock estates with the sea at Troon. The Colonel's comments on the cost of keeping up an estate appear to be based in personal experience:[153] in 1803, as he was about to set out for Trinidad, he made a Trust Disposition in favour of Charles Selkrig and others, which reveals a considerable personal debt. Parts of the estate, such as Orangefield (acquired in 1786) and Fairfield had been sold, and he was anxious to ensure that Fullarton itself was not sold.[154] In this, as in much else at the end of his life, Colonel Fullarton was to be disappointed.

Fullarton was buried in Isleworth church, in Surrey, commemorated by a marble tablet.[155] He was succeeded as the representative of this ancient family by his second–cousin Stewart Murray Fullarton of Bartonholm, who had married in 1796 Rosetta, said to be Colonel Fullarton's daughter.[156]

Colonel William Fullarton was only 54 when he died. His career never reached the heights that perhaps had been expected of it. He was undoubtedly intelligent, and with an enquiring mind, while his adventures in the sub–continent marked a sea–change in British fortunes in India. He appears to have put a financial expression of his patriotism before a proper husbanding of his own money, and the personally disastrous result of his time in Trinidad was, no doubt, partly caused by a particular view of what was 'right' for the country. Luckily for us, his lasting monument has proved to be his writing, and especially his General View of the Agriculture of the County of Ayr.

GENERAL VIEW

OF THE

AGRICULTURE

OF THE COUNTY OF

AYR,

WITH OBSERVATIONS ON THE MEANS OF ITS IMPROVEMENT.

BY COL. FULLARTON,

OF FULLARTON.

DRAWN UP FOR THE CONSIDERATION OF THE BOARD OF AGRICULTURE
AND INTERNAL IMPROVEMENT.

EDINBURGH:

PRINTED BY JOHN PATERSON.

M,DCC,XCIII.

Title page (actual page size 7 by $9^5/_8$ inches)

General View of the Agriculture of the County of Ayr

with observations on the means of its improvement
by Colonel Fullarton of Fullarton
Drawn up for the consideration of the Board of Agriculture and
Internal Improvement[157]

Advertisement

The following valuable communication, respecting the present state of husbandry in the county of Ayr, and the means of its improvement, drawn up for the consideration of the Board of Agriculture, is now printed, merely for the purpose of its being circulated there, in order that every person, interested in the welfare of that county, may have it in his power to examine it fully before it is published.[158] It is therefore requested, that any remark, or additional observation, which may occur to the reader, on the perusal of the following sheets, may be transmitted to the Board of Agriculture, at its office in London, by whom the same shall be properly attended to; and, when the returns are completed, an account will be drawn up of the state of agriculture in Ayrshire, from the information thus accumulated; which, it is believed, will be found greatly superior to any thing of the kind ever yet made public.

The Board is now following the same plan, in regard to all the other counties in the united kingdom; and, it is hardly necessary to add, will be happy to give every assistance in its power, to any person who may be desirous of improving his breed of cattle, sheep, &c. or of trying any useful experiment in husbandry.

Introduction

To Sir John Sinclair, Bart., President of the Board of Agriculture.
Fullarton, Ayrshire, Nov. 1793.

Dear Sir,

It will afford me real satisfaction, if the following observations, on the agriculture and improvement of AYRSHIRE, shall fulfil the object of your application, and prove conducive to the purposes of that valuable institution, which you have been so instrumental in establishing. Every landholder, whatever his pursuits in life may be, is bound in duty, and it is fortunate if he be also led by inclination, to promote the arts of cultivation, which form the basis of all national prosperity. Happily for this country, the superior influence of our constitution has, in no instance, been more conspicuous, than in its operation on every species of agricultural improvement. Insomuch, that, although some favoured spots, such as Lombardy and Flanders, have brought that art to an astonishing height of perfection; there is no country in Europe, where men, possessing property in land, have so generally applied their skill and capital, to the encouragement of husbandry, and the introduction of new modes of cultivation. Neither is there any circumstance, which has tended more to aggravate the signal calamities, accumulated on the landed proprietors of a neighbouring and distracted nation, than their prevailing ignorance and inattention to that useful art, which it is the pride of this country to have cherished with success; and which, under the influence of so respectable an institution as that where you preside, we may hope to see advancing to a still higher pitch of improvement.[159]

Extent

The county of AYR extends 90 miles along the western coast of Scotland, from its southern boundary, near Loch–Ryan, in Wigtonshire, to Kelly bridge, which separates it from Renfrewshire upon the north. Its breadth is in general from 20 to 25 miles. This county contains three divisions; Carrick, on the south; Coil, in the centre; and Cunningham, which includes all the northern district.

In so large a tract of country, great variety of soil prevails. On the shore it is generally light and sandy, interspersed with deep and fertile loam. A great part of the county is of a strong productive clay. In many parts a bare till or schistus extends for miles; and over it only a few inches of a better clay soil. Further up the country, there is a kind of spongy clay land, cold, wet, and obdurate; producing grass, unfit, in its present state, for fattening cattle, and merely sufficient to keep alive a breeding stock. On the eastern boundaries of the county, the land is high and moorish, intersected with mosses, bogs and marshes.

In describing the agriculture of a county so extensive as Ayrshire, it is extremely difficult to specify the various particulars respecting the soil, management, and produce, without descending to a very tedious minuteness of explanation. I am sensible, too, that this, like other geographical essays, must unavoidably be the dullest of all writings, except to those who mean to derive practical benefit from the communication. It shall, however, be my endeavour, to lay before you such a view, as may leave no material fact omitted: Conceiving it to be your object, to trace the various causes which have retarded or accelerated the progress of improvement, and to collect the statement of all that is excellent or defective in the agricultural system of every county; in order that your Board may be enabled to deduce results, and form conclusions tending to the general advantage of the kingdom.

Antient State

Before we enter on the present state of Ayrshire practice, it is essential to explain the barbarous mismanagement from whence the county has emerged;

containing, like many other parts of Scotland, and various spots in England, almost every thing that a good farmer ought to avoid.[160]   But, as acquired and rooted ignorance, is more difficult to conquer, than absence of skill or knowledge, much praise to the landholders and farmers of this county, for the very rapid progress they have already made.   A stranger, passing through these districts, must be surprised to observe such a multitude of agricultural defects still existing: But his applause would undoubtedly be excited, when he understood the great difference between the present management and that which took place forty years ago.   At that period, there was hardly a practicable road in the county; whereas, at present, few parts of the Kingdom are so well supplied in that particular.   The farm–houses were mere hovels, moated with clay, having an open hearth or fire–place in the middle; the dunghill at the door; the cattle starving; and the people wretched.   The few ditches which existed were ill constructed, and the hedges worse preserved. The land over–run with weeds and rushes, gathered into very high, broad, serpentine ridges, interrupted with large baulks, such as still disgrace the agriculture of some English counties.   The little soil there was, collected on the top of the ridge, and the furrow drowned with water.   No fallows, no green crops, no sown grass, no carts or waggons, no straw yards; hardly a potatoe, or any other esculent root, and, indeed, no garden vegetables; unless a few Scotch kail, which, with milk and oatmeal, formed the diet of the people: With little straw and no hay, except a scanty portion of the coarsest quality collected from the bogs.   The quantity of dung produced was of small avail; and that portion, little as it was, the farmers dragged on cars or sledges, or on what were called tumbler–wheels, which turned with the axletree, and supported the wretched vehicle, hardly able to draw 5 cwt.   The ground was scourged with a succession of oats after oats, as long as they would pay for seed and labour, and afford a small surplus of oatmeal for the family; and then remained in a state of absolute sterility, or over–run with thistles, till rest enabled it again to reproduce a scanty crop.

The arable farms were generally small, because the tenants had not stock for larger occupations.   A ploughgate of land, or as much as could employ four horses, allowing half of it to be ploughed, was a common sized farm.   It was often runridge or mixed property; and two or three farmers usually lived in the same place, and had their different distributions of the farm, in various proportions, from 10 to 40, 60, or 100 acres.

Many of these leases were granted for three 19 years.   The rent was frequently paid in kind, or in what was called half labour, by the steel–bow tenants, like the *Metayers* of France; the stock and implements being furnished mutually, or on such terms as could be fixed.   One half of the crop went to the landlord; and the other remained with the tenant, to maintain his family and to cultivate his farm.[o.f.] The tenants were harassed with a multitude of vexatious servitudes; such as, ploughing and leading for the landlord, working his hay, and other operations;

which, from the nature of them, unavoidably interfered with the attention necessary on the tenant's own farm. These are now almost entirely abolished.

> *Original footnote:* Of this mode, there is at present but one remaining instance in the county.[161]

The farm was divided into what was called the croft, or in–field, and the out–field land.

The croft, which commonly was a chosen spot near the house, after two or three crops of oats, received all the dung produced from the farm; and then was sown with big or four–rowed barley.[162] It then remained a year in lay; and was broke up the following season to undergo the same rotation. As to the out–field land, it remained in a state of absolute reprobation. No dung was ever spread on any part of it. The starved cattle kept on the farm, were suffered to poach the fields, from the end of Harvest, till the ensuing seedtime; and thus the roots of natural grass were cut on all the clay lands, or drowned with water standing in the cattle's footsteps.[163] The horses, during Winter, were fed on straw, on boiled chaff or weak corn, and on such hay as the bogs and marshes spontaneously produced.

As the winter seasons, in Ayrshire, are extremely wet, the plough was never yoked till Candlemas.[164] It does not appear that the farmers were in the practice of using more than four horses to each plough; but, there was a man to hold, another to drive, and a third to clear the mould board, and keep the coulter in the ground.[165] The plough was of the Scotch kind; and, as the land was generally stiff and full of stones, and never properly cultivated, it was thought necessary to construct it of the strongest and most clumsy materials. The cold and rainy springs suggested the practice of sowing extremely late, so that oats were seldom harrowed in before April; and it was not unfrequently the end of May, before the big, or four–rowed barley, was put in the ground.

As there were few or no inclosures, the horses and cattle were either *tethered*, during the Summer months, or trusted to the direction of a herd and cur–dog, by whom the poor starved animals were kept in constant agitation; being impelled, through famine, to fly from their bare lays, and commit continual depredations on the adjacent crops.

Every farmer sowed a sufficiency of flax to employ the women of his family at leisure hours. A small portion of hemp was likewise planted to make sacks and other coarse materials needed on the farm. And a quantity of wool was either bought or reared for the purpose of spinning woolen stuffs to cloath the family. These, as well as the linen were usually worked by some weaver in the neighbourhood, and supplied the dress of both sexes. The stalks of hemp were substituted in the place of candles; and, even in situations adjoining to a coalliery, whole months were wasted in cutting, drying, and leading peat; to serve as fuel.

The cattle starved during Winter, hardly able to rise without aid in Spring, and perpetually harassed during summer, never were in fit condition for the market. But undoubtedly they must have been of an admirable race and stamina, otherwise they never could have survived the treatment they experienced.

Very little butcher meat was used, excepting a proportion, which every family salted at Martinmas,[166] to serve during Winter, with their grots,[167] or prepared barley, and kail or broth. The rest of their food consisting at that time, only of porridge, oatmeal cakes, and some milk or cheese. So small was the consumption of butcher meat in this province 50 years ago, that there were not more than fifty head of cattle annually killed in the county town of Ayr, at that period, although it contained from 4 to 5000 inhabitants: And, now, there are several thousand cattle, besides great quantities of sheep, killed every year; insomuch, that it is one of the best markets in the kingdom.

Wretched as the system of management was, it is obvious, that the light, rich lands, would by no means suffer in the same proportion with the hard and tilly soils.[o.f.] On the contrary, they produced considerable quantities of grass, and kept the cattle, fed on them, in good condition.

> *Original footnote:* Till, is an obdurate schistus or clay, unmixed with
> vegetable or animal substances, and unfit for purposes of vegetation, until it
> has undergone a very long amelioration. It is of so tenacious a nature as to
> hold water, thereby chilling and drowning the plants in wet seasons; and, as
> it cracks and hardens, like a brick, in dry weather, it may be considered as
> the most unpropitious of all soils.

With respect to the moorland part of the county; as its bleak and elevated situation, with the cold, wet nature of the soil, render it by no means favourable to the growth of corn, under any mode of management, it necessarily, in those days, retained a relative barbarism with the lower districts. The moor farmers in general occupied great tracts of land. They were perfectly unacquainted with planting or inclosures. In the bottoms, some small lots of corn were cultivated, and a few loads of coarse hay obtained from the meadows. The farms were stocked with a proportion of black cattle, which when fat, did not weigh more than 16 or 20 stone English; and with a small hardy race of wild, black–faced sheep, weighing when fat, about 10 lb English per quarter, and yielding not more than two or three pounds of very coarse wool per fleece. The moor farmers having hardly any fodder, and no green feeding for their sheep and cattle, the flock was regulated by the number that could be subsisted in hard weather.

The state of markets was in general so low, and public credit so ill established, that no tenant could command money to stock his farm; and few landholders could raise the means of improving their estates. Indeed, when a laird wished to raise money, he was obliged to sell his property, perhaps for 20 years purchase, or accept of loans on wadset: the nature of the obligation being, that if the money was not repaid within a specified time, the land became the property of the lender.[168]

There were no manufactures in the county, excepting of bonnets at Stewarton, and of shoes and carpets at Kilmarnock. Exports and imports from the harbours of Ayr, Irvine, and Saltcoats, were on a very small scale indeed.[169] In general, the finest lands were let for 2 or 3 shillings per acre; and there was neither skill, capital, industry, nor credit in the country to do away the wretchedness described.[of]

> *Original footnote:* It is, however, true, that some rich holms and bottoms paid in kind to the extent even of two bolls of bear or big per acre.

The consequences of such mismanagement were truly deplorable. The people having hardly any substitute for oatmeal, were entirely at the mercy of the season. If the seedtime was unfavourable, the summer bad, or the autumn late and stormy; a dearth or famine unavoidably ensued. The price of meal fluctuated, therefore, between extremes, which are never known in countries better cultivated; or where the means of subsistence are so varied, as to render the failure of one species suppliable by some other.[of] At the beginning of this century, and end of the last, there was a succession of bad seasons which lasted several years, and reduced the county of Ayr, and other provinces adjacent, to the lowest gradation of want; obliging hundreds of families to fly for subsistence to the north of Ireland, where their descendants still remain. At that time, the price of oatmeal rose to 2s 6d per peck, weighing 8 lb 10 oz English.

> *Original footnote:* Frequently from 6d to 1s 6d per peck, whereas, under the present improved mode of cultivation, it seldom varies more than 1d or 2d above, or below 1s per peck.

In those seasons of misery, the poor people have not infrequently been obliged to subsist by bleeding their cattle, and mixing the blood so procured, with what oatmeal they could procure.[of]

> *Original footnote:* On reading this description, one would think it applied to the dark and gloomy periods of the lower ages, when the best fields in Italy were desolate; and when the north of Europe, under barbarous landlords, with serfs or bondsmen for their cultivators, exhibited those scenes of ignorance and indigence, so emphatically described by Sigonius and Potgesserus.[170]

Change of System

In a country, such as Scotland, where soil and climate, in many instances, unite to counteract the endeavours of the cultivator; it required extraordinary exertions indeed, to bring the county of Ayr in so short a time from the degradation already stated, to that period of improvement, which, if continued for a few years longer, will entitle it to rank amongst the most productive districts in Great Britain.

The means by which this important change has been effected, require to be detailed. The landed property of Ayrshire was parcelled out among a multitude of proprietors, under very different descriptions; from the petty feuar or emphyteutical[171] holder, paying a fixed rent in perpetuity, for a house and garden, through all the gradations of vassals holding the property of farms, and paying quit rents to subjects–superior; and of persons who according to the feudal titles of Scotland, held estates *in capite** under the crown, from a few acres to 100,000, which is the largest in the county.*o.f.* In short, the tenures by which land was held, were various as the extent and value of the different estates.

> *Original footnote:* Those feuars, of whom there are many in the country, probably paid the current rent for their feus at the time they were granted, and in some cases perhaps more. But such has been the rise in the value of landed property, that these feu duties, now, are so perfectly disproportioned to the actual rent, that they are little more than a mere acknowledgment, that the land is held of the subject superior. It has always occurred to me that if landholders chuse to grant feus, in perpetuity for a rent certain, which is at best an improvident transaction, the rent should be specified, not in coin, which varies in its value but in grain, which at all times must necessarily be the permanent standard of value in every country.[172]

The small proprietor of 50 or 100 acres, was seldom sufficiently active or intelligent to introduce amelioration. Contented with the produce of his fields, on the old system, he left improvements to the upper order of proprietors. The medium lairds, or country gentlemen, were frequently driven by their situations and professions into various quarters of the globe; and were no less distinguished by their enlightened education, than by their intelligence and success in various walks of life. But their habits and observations had hardly ever been applied to the best of all purposes, the cultivation of their native soil. Any attempts they made were feeble, desultory, and unavailing; while the great lords and large proprietors possessed such extensive tracts of uncultivated land, that to attempt a general system of improvement appeared beyond their means: Neither was any plan thought of, for bringing the active exertions of the landed interest into one point of

---

* in chief.

union and effect. On the contrary, deep rooted prejudices against innovation prevailed, especially amongst the inferior classes of renters and proprietors. The tenant considered all amelioration as tending only to augment his labour and increase his rent. If any landholder was hardy enough occasionally to attempt improvement, he had every possible obstacle to contend with. Labourers were ignorant and indolent. Stock, and implements, entirely inadequate and inapplicable to rational principles of husbandry, and much time, labour, and expence, were wasted before any benefit could be derived from an improved mode of cultivation, in a country where the common elements of farming were rude and barbarous. No wonder, then, if those who first essayed the arduous undertaking were disappointed in their hopes, and commonly impaired the property they meant to increase.

Fortunately, however, the country possessed within itself the means of improvement in a superior degree. Extensive tracts of very rich and valuable land; abundance of coal and lime, almost in every quarter; a number of towns and villages; which, although at that time destitute of arts and manufactures, were however commodiously situated, and scattered over the different districts of the county.

Exertions of Individuals

But these advantages might long have continued dormant, had they not been called forth by the superior energies of a few individuals, to whom the present advancement of the county is chiefly due.

About 40 years ago, the late Earl of Eglinton, who possessed a very large and valuable property, dispersed over a great extent, in the most improveable parts of Ayrshire, resolved to rescue his estates from the condition in which he found them.[173] An eminent farmer, Mr Wight of Ormiston, was brought from East Lothian to introduce the proper mode of ploughing, levelling ridges, fallowing, drilling, turnip husbandry, and rotations of crop.[174] Great attention was bestowed on the breed of horses and cattle. Ploughmen and dairy people were brought from various parts of England. Fences were made on an extensive scale, and the county was beautified by a multitude of clumps, belts, and plantations. The noblemen and gentlemen very zealously concurred in promoting measures so conducive to their own advantage and to the general interest of their country. The demand for cheese and butter to supply the multiplying wants of Glasgow, Paisley, Greenock, and Port–Glasgow, led to increasing care respecting milch cows and dairies.[175] The English market afforded ready sale for black cattle; and the growing manufactures of the country introduced the benefits of opulence.

Increasing Opulence—Establishment of Banks

These concurring circumstances gave rise to private or county banks and paper circulation; and by their means the landholders, whose security was good, but who were in general destitute of ready money, were enabled to discount bills, procure cash accompts, and establish other modes of credit for the improvement of their estates.[176] At the same time, industrious tenants, joining together as securities for each other, were accommodated with money to stock and cultivate their farms. Whatever disadvantages may result from an overstrained circulation of paper currency, or incautious extension of credit; yet, in this instance, the effects of such pecuniary accommodations were truly beneficial. In a very short time, good turnpike roads were completed in every direction; wheel–carriages were gradually introduced; coallieries and lime quarries were opened; draw–kilns erected; almost every field was divided by hedge and ditch; good farm–houses were constructed; sown grasses prevailed; the breed of animals was improved; the lowest class of people were enabled to live better, by the introduction and general use of potatoes. The seat of every considerable person was ornamented with planting, and his fields improved; and there hardly remained a proprietor, of any condition whatever, who did not, in some form or other, promote the interesting work of cultivation.

Obstacles to Improvement

Great as these advantages appear, they were inadequate to produce the superior benefits which the county has attained. It is to be observed, that, notwithstanding the advancement already mentioned, agriculture remained almost without a beacon or directory to guide its course, or specify its progress. Much advantage had indeed been derived from imitating the better practice of East–Lothian, and some of the well managed provinces in England. But the mode of agriculture, established in these places, presupposed skill and industry in the labourer, stock and knowledge in the farmer, and a regulated cultivation; without which the best blessings of soil and climate will prove unavailing. Besides, the indiscriminate adoption of plans and systems, formed for other districts, soils, and climates, was liable to infinite objections. For example, the ingenious Secretary of your Board maintains, that the only mode, by which a scientific or successful husbandry can any where be established, is by granting extensive farms to opulent and skillful tenants. But, in the present instance, this became impracticable; because, without alluding to the necessary portion of industry and skill, few tenants had stock and implements sufficient for 80 or 100 acres. It is farther to be observed, that in a soil and climate where ploughing, sowing, reaping, and stacking corn, are liable to constant interruptions; it is hardly possible for any farmer to manage, without loss, a large quantity of land in tillage; and, at any rate, it tends to diminish the number of farmers and their families, substituting hinds and cottagers, and labouring servants in their place.[o.f.]

Original footnote: Pliny's opinion on this subject is expressed in the following words: "Modum agri inprimis servandum antiqui putavere.

Quippe ita censebant, satius esse minus serere et melius arare."[177]* And
Virgil says, "Laudato ingentia rura exiguum colito."[178]†

When the practice of winter–ploughing, so prevalent in dryer climates and
in lighter soils, was attempted on the deep and tilly parts of Ayrshire, the land was
so drenched as to yield a scanty produce. In like manner, numberless improvers
lost their crops by sowing early, in imitation of their southern neighbours; and
many a field of clay, by summer fallowing in a rainy season, was rendered only fit
to be converted into brick or mortar. When the high and crooked ridges were
attempted to be cleaved and levelled, the productive soil was buried, and a sterile
till was thrown upon the surface; which, having been excluded from the air, and
unmixed with any animal or vegetable substance, required a long course of
ploughing, manure, and exposure to the atmosphere, before it could afford the
pabulum of vegetation:[179] Insomuch, that the tract of old ridges is frequently is
marked with barrenness, at this day, in fields, which, after being levelled, have for
20 years undergone a successive course of cultivation. In short, when any person,
implicitly adopting the management of other counties, laid no other limitations
upon his tenants than such as were adapted to places, where the land was already
dressed and drained, the soil and climate dry, and a proper rotation of crops
established; he was invariably disappointed in his object; and the farm, at the
mercy of unrestrained and unskilful tillage, became little better than a caput
mortuum.‡

In this situation the wisest cultivator around Ghent, Bruges, or Alost, would
have found himself perplexed. His endeavours to lay the land clean, and dry, by
straight furrows, well–proportioned ridges, and frequent drills, would have been
frustrated, or at best have proved a tedious and expensive undertaking, in a country
where the ridges were high, crooked, full of stones and baulks; where every furrow
was like a ditch, and every head–ridge a mound to prevent the outlet of the water.

Had he brought the best ploughmen from Norfolk, who, at home, with two
horses, will work near two acres daily, he would have found them soon conform to
the Ayrshire complement of 3 roods; while the native labourer would have learned
from his instructors, to refuse employment on any other work. In vain would he
have attempted to save his land from poaching, and to increase manure by feeding
every animal upon the farm within doors, as is the practice of the Netherlands. It
would have required years before he could get into a course of clover, sainfoin,

---

* The people of ancient times thought that observing moderation in the size of a farm was
    especially important, in as much as it was their belief that it was more advantageous
    to sow less land and plough it better. (Plin. Nat. Hist. XVIII, 7, 35.)

† Praise large estates, but cultivate a small one. (Virg. Georg. II, 412, 413.)

‡ Literally a dead head; i.e. lost investment, money down the drain.

vetches, tares, and lucerne, for summer feeding; and into cole, cabbage, carrots, turnips, rape, and oilcakes for winter. And, after all, he would have found neither shed nor straw–yard on the farm, in which his stock could be accommodated.

New System introduced

Under these difficulties, it was fortunate for the county, that a gentleman of considerable property, united with great abilities and observation (Mr Fairly of Fairly[180]), devoted his attention to the gradual correction of abuses, which no power or influence could at once abolish. Knowing the imperfect nature of the instruments he had to work with, he determined to proceed by a less rapid, but more certain, operation. Every farm, as it came out of lease, was inclosed and divided by sufficient fences into three or more parts, and was allowed to remain in grass, till it recovered from the exhausting course of evil management already stated.[of] About 100 bolls of slacked lime were spread upon the sward of each acre. A convenient house and offices were completed, and in this condition, it was ready for a tenant.

> *Original footnote:* The Ayrshire boll of lime contains 4 Winchester bushels, costing, at the draw kill, from 3d to 5d and 6d per boll.

But, in order to preserve the benefits so tediously and expensively acquired, the most pointed limitations were necessary; not only to prevent the farmer from reducing his land by bad management, to its former wretched situation, but to enforce a rational system of amendment.

The lease was usually granted for 18 years; and the covenants obliged the tenant, not to plough more than one third of the farm in any one year nor to plough the same land more than three years successively. With the third crop, the tenant was bound to sow 3 bushels of ryegrass, and 12 lb of clover. To cut it for hay only one year, and pasture 5, before the same could be ploughed again. The tenant was bound to keep the houses in repair, to maintain the gates and fences; and in case of failure, the landlord might employ labourers, and charge the amount with the next year's rent. The fodder was stipulated to be consumed upon the ground, and all the manure to be spread upon it. Heavy additional rents were specified for every acre ploughed beyond the limitation: And these rents were not in the form of penalties, but as a compensation for the very serious loss incurred by cropping the ground beyond the periods admitted by the lease.

In confirmation of these remarks, it is to be observed that the same ground which in pasture yields 20s per acre, is frequently worth £5 or £6 per acre, annually for 3 years' ploughing. It is not surprising, therefore, that any attempts to invalidate the course of such covenants by appealing against the right of landlords to impose limitations on their tenants, should have excited the strongest feelings of alarm, and occasioned impressions of positive wrong on the minds of all persons, connected with the landed interest, whose properties might be injured to the amount of many hundreds per cent, and reduced to their ancient sterility, if the courts of justice were to cease supporting these covenants.

Under the regulations specified by Mr Fairlie, there never could be more than one–third of the farm in crop; and no land could be ploughed till it had lain six years in grass.[181] The produce on one–third of the farm so ploughed, was usually double or triple that which the whole yielded under the old management of croft and out–field land. The remaining two–thirds being sown down with all the lime, dung, and manure, that could be collected, afforded a supply of hay, and grass, more valuable than the whole produce of the farm under the antient system. Those farmers, who persisted in raising three successive crops of oats, undoubtedly, scourged the land as much as could be done in three years, or as could well be recovered by six years of rest under sown grass. But many farmers had sense enough to take beans and pease as the second crop, and to sow big or barley, and grass seeds for the third; by which means the land has been brought into a condition capable of yielding crops hardly equalled, and certainly not surpassed in any part of Great Britain. The same Gentleman, having fortunately undertaken the superintendence of the estates of the present Earl of Eglintoun, and applied his system to the management of that extensive property; in the space of little more than 20 years, has established a reformation so complete, that it is universally adopted almost on every arable estate in Ayrshire.[182] The consequences are, abundant crops of grain; plentiful returns of hay; and the finest pasture where little or no pasture grew before. Indeed, the principle of not allowing more than three successive crops to be taken off the same field, without rest or intervening fallow, and of sowing grass seeds along with the third and last crops, is so completely established, that the tenant attempting to depart from that course, without stipulation, would be held, by the judicial country courts, as acting wrongfully to the proprietor, and an interdict would be obtained against him, on the principle that he was deviating from the usage of the country, to the detriment of the proprietor, who is understood to let the use but not the abuse of the land.

State of Property

The division of property, as has been already stated, is extremely various; and the different circumstances, respecting its extent and distribution, are expressed in a column annexed to the map which accompanies this paper.[183]
A great proportion of the landed estates have changed their owners in consequence of individual extravagance, expensive engagements, and the distress occasioned by the failure of the Ayr bank in the year 1772.[184]
The run–ridge and mingled property, is now almost entirely divided, and unless around some burghs and villages; and, in a few other instances, there are no common lands in county.[o.f]

Original footnote: There are three tenures of land in this county, which, from their uncommonness, deserve to be recorded. The first is of the Lands of Priestwick, on the coast of Coil, erected into a burgh by very antient charters; under the direction of a chancellor, baillies, and other borough officers. There are about 1000 acres of land divided among 36 freemen, or barons as they are called. Each possesses a lot of arable ground, and a right of pasturing a specified number of sheep and cattle on the common. The lots do not remain in perpetuity with any one possessor, but are appropriated from time to time by drawing for them at the end of a certain number of years; and no freeman can sell his property without consent of the corporation. The next tenure, is that of Newton upon Ayr, very accurately described by the Rev. Mr Peebles, in his Statistical Report of that parish, already published. The property belonging to the community contains about 200 arable acres, divided among 48 freemen, and 150 acres in common among them. The last, and most remarkable, consists of 240 acres of rich land, held by 40 persons in lots of 6 acres each, adjoining to Kilmaurs, (which was erected into a burgh of barony under King James V.) under a charter granted by the Earl of Glencairn 1577; the holders paying at the rate of 2 merks for each 40th part. By this charter, the Earl of Glencairn binds himself to allow no articles of manufacture to be made on the estate, nor any article of produce to be sold, excepting in the said burgh of barony.[185] His object undoubtedly was by these restrictive grants and privileges, to allure ingenious tradesmen to the burgh of Kilmaurs. But his intentions were frustrated; for the tradesmen so established, and their descendants, have generally forsaken the business of handicraft, and employed themselves in cultivating their respective lots, which still continue run–ridge. On this land, for many years, were raised plants of Scotch kail, so valuable that great part of Scotland was supplied with them; but in no other respect has either agriculture or manufacture benefited by these three institutions. The particulars of this charter, and the strange tenure in question, are accurately stated by the Rev. Mr Millar in his excellent Statistical account of the parish of Kilmaurs.[186]

The proprietors are unacquainted with many obstacles to improvement, which exist in the southern part of the island. The land–tax, together with conversion of statute labour for repairing of roads, minister's stipend, and salaries to schoolmasters, are the only assessments to which the lands are subjected. These are usually made payable by the tenant, over above the rent specified in his lease; and seldom amount to more than 2 or 3 per cent, of the actual rent.

Value of the Land—Produce—Kinds of Grain

The light sandy links, and downs along the shore, being unfit for tillage, ought either to be planted, or let in rabbit warren, which yields near 10s per acre, while it is hardly worth 5s for pasture. The flat and arable parts ought to be covered with 200 or 300 cart loads of clay; and the practice of folding or flaking sheep on turnips as a preparative for barley and grass–seeds, is found an eligible system.[o.f.] Potatoes, and all the kinds of Scotch kail, or curled greens, also succeed extremely well. These lands, under such management, are worth from 10s to 20s per acre, according to the staple of the soil. The better quality of strong clays are generally let from 20s to 30s per acre; and loams, or rich gravel, from 30s to 40s.

> *Original footnote:* This system has not only been found extremely beneficial in many parts of England, but is recommended by the best farmers of antiquity. "Ubi sementim facturus eris, ibi oves delectato, et frondem usque ad pabula matura." Cato XXX.[187*] And Pliny says, "Sunt qui optime stercorari putent, sub dio retibus inclusa pecorum mansione." Plin. Nat. Hist. XVIII, 53, 194.[†]

On these soils, it is not unusual circumstance to raise 10 to 12 Winchester quarters of oats; 6 and 8 quarters of big or barley, and as much of beans, for which the soil of Ayrshire is in many places admirably adapted; although the wetness of the harvests renders it difficult to dry them. But this is in a great measure obviated by letting them remain till they become black and dry before they are cut. Beans are found to succeed well on lay; and it will be fortunate for the county, if the practice of using them, as an intervening crop between oats and barley shall become more general. Many farmers approve of sowing pease along with beans, which cover the land more completely; but it must be the late kind of pease, otherwise they will not ripen with the beans.

Pease alone, though sometimes a productive crop in this county, are extremely troublesome to dry, occasioned by the wetness of the climate; neither do they usually yield more per acre than 5 or 6 bolls of four Winchester bushels each, worth about one guinea per boll.[188]

Turnips

There are not yet above a score of common farmers in the county who are in the practice of raising turnips. Their crops, however, prove extremely luxuriant, and several of them have adopted the best mode yet extant of using turnips,

---

[*] On land where you intend to sow, keep your sheep in their folds and feed them leaves until the forage crop is full–grown.

[†] Some people think that the best method of manuring land is to keep their flocks out of doors and penned in with netting.

namely, to draw every alternate turnip, and feed cattle with them in the house; to fold sheep and young stock on the remainder; and whenever a turnip is broken or spoiling, to draw it for the stall–fed cattle. By these means, the whole produce is turned to account; whereas in other places the finest crops are frequently destroyed in rainy seasons, for want of common care and skill.

Wheat

Wheat is not a crop in general practice; but those who raise it, whenever they take pains to clean their land, have good returns, usually from 4 to 6 Winchester quarters per acre. The red wheat is often sown, although the fine early Essex, Hertford, or Suffolk seed–wheat is preferable.[189] But unless the grain be steeped in brine, we find it apt to blight and blacken. The wheat raised in Ayrshire is of an excellent quality, often weighing from 60 to 63 lb per bushel; yet the cultivation of this grain is liable to great objection. The summers are frequently so wet, and the harvest so late and stormy, that a large tract of land cannot properly be prepared for wheat, without a greater power of men and horses, than belongs to ordinary farmers. If ever it succeeds on an extensive scale, it must be after clover; the land having been previously enriched and cleaned with turnips, followed by barley, which, when good in this country, never fail to ensure a fine succeeding crop.

Rotation of Crops

Of all the rotations hitherto discovered, the best for Ayrshire appears to be from lay, oats, or beans.[o.f.] After these, in dry soils, turnips or other green crops, such as kail, vetches, tares, and potatoes. In. very strong soils drilled beans, cabbages, and carrots, may be substituted in the place of turnips. These followed by a crop of barley sown with grass–seeds. After the clover, wheat, or oats, and in very light lands, rye. By this mode, it is presumed, that wheat may be cultivated on a large scale with advantage. For if the harvest prove so wet, that the intended portion of land cannot be sown with winter wheat, it only requires sowing a larger quantity of oats or spring wheat, and still continuing the same rotation.

> *Original footnote:* Beans, on old rested lay, frequently yield 6 Winchester quarters per acre; worth about 32s per quarter.

Potatoes

The culture of potatoes is so universally established in every part of this county, that the poorest labourers, and the most extensive farmers, raise a sufficiency for their own consumption. It is observed, that so far from exhausting the land, potatoes, when luxuriant, are sure to be succeeded by an abundant crop. Various kinds of them are cultivated; but the round red and the round white of a dry nature are preferred, both for taste and produce. They are generally sold for 6d per peck, weighing 36 lb, or 8 shillings per boll of 16 pecks; and the value of £16 or £20, is not infrequently gathered off an acre. In short, of all the benefits, the lower classes of the community have acquired within the present century in this county, the general cultivation of potatoes is probably the most important. Lazy beds are almost entirely laid aside; and the potatoes are planted in the month of June, on land prepared by the plough, manured and drilled like other green crops, and are lifted before there be danger of the frost destroying them.*o.f.*

> *Original footnote:* The prejudices against potatoes have been found in many places almost unconquerable. An idea of their being a species of solanum, and consequently unwholesome, prevented their cultivation in Italy.[190] And in France they were reckoned by the common people only fit for swine; until the celebrated Comptroller General, Mr Turgot, exerted his influence, and introduced them while Intendant of Limoges, by ordering dishes of them in different forms to be regularly served at his own table every day.[191]

Big and Barley

The Ayrshire farmers very frequently prefer big to barley. The average weight of the former is only 48 lb per Winchester bushel; while the latter is estimated at 52 lb per bushel. But the big, having four rows instead of two, is more productive, and is likewise hardier and quicker in its vegetation; so that it maybe later sown. This often proves a material advantage in such a climate, where the land for barley can seldom be prepared before the month of May; although it is thereby prevented from ripening till the beginning of September, which interferes with the oat harvest. Besides, till of late, the maltsters did not allow a price adequate to the difference of value between big and barley. But now, when barley sells at 25s per quarter, big may be had 4 or 5 shillings cheaper; although it is difficult to discover any difference in the ale brewed from these sorts of grain.

Oats

With respect to oats, which form the great staple of provisions in the county, it may safely be asserted, that, in point of quality and produce, no county in the kingdom surpasses Ayrshire. Those produced from lay are of the best and most farinacious quality. The second crop is usually better than the third. This grain being extremely impoverishing, farmers ought to learn that two crops of it should never be taken successively from any field. The time of sowing is usually from the middle to the end of March.*o.f.*

> *Original footnote:* The usual rule in better climates, is to sow the cold wet lands early, reserving the warm dry bottoms till the last of the seedtime. Cato says: "Ubi quisque locus frigidissimus, aquosissimusque

erit, ibi primum serito. In calidissimis locis sementim postremum fieri oportet." Cato XXXIV.[*] Whoever adopts this advice in Ayrshire is sure, in a wet seedtime, to impair his crop. For, in this country, we must follow Pliny's rule, Never to touch land when wet: "Lutosam terram ne tangito." Plin. Nat. Hist. XVIII, 49, 176.[†]

Much pains are taken to procure the best qualities of seed. The old kind of small grey Scotch oats did not yield much farina. The Dutch and Polish oats, although they ripen near a fortnight earlier than the common sorts, are extremely apt to shake with heavy winds; and are, besides, much thicker in the husks than the oats now cultivated in this county.[192] These were originally raised on a bleak farm in Berwickshire called Blainsley, cleaned with great care, and sold for seed all over Scotland.[193] They do not ripen very early; and the oat harvest seldom commences sooner than September, and does not finish before October.

Weight of Grain

The average weight is 36 lb per bushel, which will produce meal at the rate of 18 pecks per Winchester quarter, each peck of meal weighing 8 lb 10 oz English weight, at 16 oz per pound. Upon the rich warm lands near the coast, no less than 22 pecks of meal have been produced from a quarter of oats. Farther up the country, the proportion will hardly exceed 16 pecks from 1 quarter of oats; and, in bad seasons, on the bleak parts of the moors, there will hardly be a return of 14 pecks of meal from a quarter of oats.

No fact can more clearly shew the absurdity of selling grain by measure instead of weight. For it is obvious that a quarter of oats, yielding 21 pecks of meal, is exactly worth 1½ quarter, yielding only 14 pecks of meal. This I took the liberty of suggesting to a member of the Privy Council, when the late corn bill was in agitation; and accompanied the statement with many observations on the subject, from an ingenious friend of mine, very deeply conversant in the corn trade. The good sense, however, of the Ayrshire farmers has at last adjusted this business, as well as could have been accomplished by the wisest legislative regulation. And now, bargains of grain are usually taken at a specified average weight, namely, at 36 lb per bushel of oats, or 18 pecks of meal per quarter. When the grain weighs less, there is a diminution in the price, at the rate of 6d in the boll, for every pound of meal defaulting. If gentlemen in different parts of England essay their oats, they will find them seldom equal to this average; and the oats from Ireland, imported into Ayr, Irvine, and Saltcoats, are commonly sold 1s or 1s 6d per quarter cheaper than Ayrshire oats.[o.f.]

---

[*] Wherever the ground is coldest and wettest, sow there first. In the warmest places you should put in the seeds last.

[†] Do not touch muddy ground.

Original footnote: The average price of oats in Ayrshire is about 16s per Winchester quarter, or 1s per peck of meal. When meal is lower, farmers can hardly pay their rents, and when much dearer, the poor are oppressed.

Chipping and Steeping Seed

In a climate such as this, when seedtime and harvest are constantly too late, several weeks might be gained by chipping or steeping the seed in moisture, and then covering it up under cloths or sacks in a barn or other warm place, for a few days, till it buds: by which means there will be the double advantage of proving the quality of the seed before it be sown, and of obtaining several weeks in its time of ripening. This mode is very generally practised in several parts of Russia;*o.f.* and I have known it with advantage applied to some kinds of grain and grass–seeds. Barley being a seed that very readily sprouts, and is usually sown in warm weather, will perhaps gain less by this practice, than beans, pease, oats, and other spring corn; and as for winter corn, the experiment would be preposterous.

In Russia the Guinea or Indian corn is raised by this mode, and might, I doubt not, be brought to sufficient perfection in this climate, to act at least as a green crop, affording the finest of all green feeding for cattle.[194] I have raised it to its full size in the open ground at this place; and it only requires, like potatoes, and other delicate productions of warm climates, not to be planted out while there is risk of frost.

Reaping and Mode of Preserving Corn

There is perhaps no county in the kingdom where the farmers are so handy and expert in reaping and managing their corns in rainy weather. The oats and barley are usually cut for 5s per Scots acre, and put in shocks for 1s more.[195] The stubble is cut extremely short, and no corn is left to encourage gleaners and other pilferers. Besides the usual complement of farm servants, an additional number are engaged for the harvest, or the whole may be contracted for at a certain rate per acre. Even in the most humid seasons it is extremely rare to find any corn lost, or much damaged; for the farmers are constantly turning and curing it, so as to prevent its rotting, even when the rains continue so severe for many weeks, as to render it impossible to take in the corn.

Threshing–Appraising

When thoroughly dried, it is put up in stacks, containing each from 10 to 20 quarters. One of these is thrown into the barn, and threshed out as occasion may require.*o.f.* Clean oats growing on clay and soil free from weeds, may be threshed, and the straw trussed up for 10d per quarter. But oats on foul and grassy soils are dearer. The usual practice, however, is, to employ the farm servants in winter mornings to thresh from 5 to 8; when they rub down their horses, and go to out door work.

> *Original footnote:* The *Birley–men*, or appraisers, are so expert in their valuation of corn in the shock, that on a field of 50 acres, they will estimate the produce within a few bushels. They cast and thresh every 20th or 40th sheaf, which gives them the average of the whole. On the same principle, an attentive farmer, when he stacks his corn, ought to note the number of sheafs, and prove them in a similar mode. By these means he can exactly know the amount of grain contained in every stack, and prevent the possibility of imposition.

Threshing Machines

The useful invention of a threshing machine has already been introduced into the county, and is found of superior utility.[196] The principle upon which this mill performs, is by two cylinders or rollers turning quickly, and so placed, as to let all the straw pass through, and strip it from the grain. One of these machines to work with two horses, may be erected for £30 or £40.[o.f.] It requires the attendance of three men, and will thresh 3 quarters of oats per hour so clean, that not one grain of corn remains upon the stalk. It enables a farmer to supply an unexpected demand, and to prevent the continual depredations to which every farmer is exposed, when a number of labourers have constant access to his barn.

> *Original footnote:* It may also be worked by water, when there is a proper fall, or power at hand.

Multures

Multures or servitudes to particular milns are in general abolished; and with a few exceptions, every farmer takes his grain to the miller who serves him best. In some parts of the county, however, a contrary practice still prevails. The usual price for drying and grinding, is 6d per quarter of oats. Drying, steeping, and malting barley, 2s. And wheat is milled for 2s per quarter.

Hay

With respect to the culture and management of hay, notwithstanding the great quantities raised in all parts of the county, the whole system is still deficient. Instead of sowing 12 lb weight per acre of the best red clover, 6 lb of white or Dutch, and 4 lb of yellow clover, with some plantain and other meadow grasses; it is usual to sow no more than 6 or 7 lb of red clover, along with 1 or 2 bushels of ill chosen ryegrass, the greatest part of which is only an annual plant; although there be perennial ryegrass of superior quality; and all kinds of ryegrass are considered as a scourging crop.

It often happens, indeed, that the seed–merchants impose a weed called goose–grass on the farmers, and thus the fields are poisoned and impoverished.[197] The clover is seldom sown equal, but only with one cast of seed to a ridge, and the furrows being frequently wet; it is not usual to find a strong and regular crop of clover among ordinary tenants.

Grass meant to be preserved for hay is almost constantly allowed to stand so long that the seeds are formed and the juices dried. This exhausts the land, deprives the hay of nutriment, and throws the hay harvest so late, that the autumnal rains commonly take place before it be concluded. The consequences are, great expense in the working, turning, and coiling, and drying it after a succession of showers, till the whole juice and substance is exhausted; and at last, it is frequently in a state fit for nothing but litter.

The usual prices are 4d per stone for sown–grass–hay in the rick, and 6d for old hay. Notwithstanding these remarks, 200 or 300 stone per acre, is not an unusual crop.

Pasture

Much improvement might also be made for the purposes of pasture by proper attention to cultivate the most valuable meadow grasses, such as timothy, fescue, plantain, and many others suited to the different soils. It is even not improbable that the Guinea grass, although the native of a very warm country, might be brought to assimilate with this soil and climate. At present, the seeds and roots of the worst kinds of grass and weeds, are so predominant throughout the county, that they choak the more valuable sorts when sown. This evil can hardly be eradicated till drills, fallows, and green crops become an established part of the system; and rotation of husbandry in every farm.[o.f.1] Neither has it been possible, for any farmer in the county, to extirpate sprits and rushes. When once rooted in the land, they are so continually nourished by the moisture of the climate, as well as the congenial nature of the soil, and their fibres are understood to be of so imperishable a texture; that after repeated drainings, and fallowings, they have sprung in full vigour as soon as the ground returned to grass.[o.f.2]

> *Original footnote 1:* The Romans were in use to fallow every alternate year, and reckoned *terra restibilis*,* or ground which could bear crops every year extremely uncommon, and chiefly confined to the rich territory of Campania. On the other hand, the Chinese never allow any to remain in fallow or in pasture. See Voyages d'un Philosphe, par Le Poivre.[198] How would a Chinese be confounded, says this author, if he beheld our wastes, and downs and commons; our ill–dressed ridges, useless fallows, and bare fields!

---

* Land that is sown or tilled every year.

Original footnote 2: The antient georgical writers, particularly Columella,[199] Pliny, and Palladius,[200] all concur in representing rushes and other plants of a similar nature, as indications of a fertile soil. COL. lib. ii. cap. 11. PLIN. Nat. Hist. lib. 18. cap. 6. PAL. lib. 1. tit. 5.]

The pasture in this county, however, is growing richer and better every day. White clover grows spontaneously. The ground has a natural tendency to the production of grass; and there is little doubt of its rivalling the best closes of Cheshire or of Yorkshire, as soon as the land is dry; the cattle restrained from poaching it in Winter; and the practice of topdressing pasture with dung, sea–weed, lime and compost generally introduced. At present, grass lands let, in the more cultivated parts, from 15s to 30s per acre. On the bare unimproved clay soils, from 5s to 10s, while the hills and moors remain in their primitive sterility; and probably, do not average more than 1s or 1s 6d per acre.

State of Tillage

The actual state of tillage or mode of working the land, forms the next object of attention. The ridges still continue in many places very high and broad, the furrows being often 20, 30, and 40 feet asunder. In order to correct the evils of high ridges, without incurring the detriment of burying the good soil, and exposing an unfertile one, an ingenious gentleman, of great landed property, proposes a method founded on the simple principle of reducing the lowest part to a level.[o.f.] With this view, he throws off the top soil with a spade from about 6 feet at the end of a ridge, extending the whole breath across the ridge. He then proceeds to throw the top soil, from the next 6 feet upon the surface so levelled; and advances with this sort of trenching till the whole field is reduced, keeping the producing soil at top, and making the process perform the purpose of a regular trenching, equal in respect of pulverising to 4 or 5 ploughings, and effected for 40s or 50s per acre. A more simple, cheap, and efficacious operation can hardly be imagined; and no county can possibly stand more in need of such a practice than the one in question.

Original footnote: Mr Ferguson of Pitfour, Member for Aberdeenshire.[201]

Trenching

Indeed, it long has been a doubt whether the system of working land by spading and trenching, so as to bring every field to a more pulverized state by the labour of man, to the exclusion of animals, is not one of the greatest improvements which can occur in any country. Without presuming to pronounce upon a point so often agitated, it is obvious, that the land by such a process is completely cleaned, freed from stones, levelled, and pulverized. That the produce of garden stuffs, green crops, grain, and grass, is thus rendered far superior to the ordinary mode by tillage; that besides the advantage of employing the human species in place of the brute creation, the expense is little different. For example, to plough or fallow a field five times, with two horses and a driver, costs in Ayrshire between 30s and 40s per acre. To half trench an acre, with one spading and a shoveling, will cost about the same money; and a double trenching, with two spadings and two shovelings, in ordinary soil does not exceed 50s or £3 per acre.

The return from such management is truly surprising. Acres so worked have been known to yield above 60 bolls of potatoes each; and a farmer near Grougar and Kilmarnock, a few years ago, on land prepared with double trenching, raised a crop of wheat, for which he received £19 per acre.

A still larger produce has frequently been raised on deep rich land, prepared with double trenching, and planted with the round hard–headed Scotch cabbage, and rows of beans between the intervals. But these instances cannot occur unless when the ground is well manured, and great attention bestowed on procuring seed of the best quality, and plants in full vigour; as there is probably no part of farming in which more loss acrues from indolence and ignorance, than in the careless choice of seed, and selection of plants.

Ploughing

But to return to ploughing.[202] Every rational farmer in this county is sensible, at last, of the advantages derived from straight furrows, the ridges just sloping sufficiently to direct the water to the furrows, and not more than 12 feet wide. By this proportion, the field is laid entirely dry; the ridge may be sown at two castings, reaped with two sickles a–breast, and mowed with one scythe at two turns.

In this county, as in several others, the modes of ploughing are various, and in many cases exceptionable. In light easy soils, devoid of stones, like different parts of Norfolk, the art of ploughing is so simple, that it may be performed almost in any way, and effected by a plough of any common construction. But, when the light, broad bottomed Norfolk plough, is used in the stiff stoney soils of Ayrshire, the work is most imperfectly performed. The object in this county is to make a furrow from 4 to 6 inches deep, according to the nature of the soil. In order to lay that furrow neatly up, shouldering to the next, it is necessary that the flake or furrow be at least one third wider than its depth. If it were only as broad as deep, it would be exactly a square; and the furrow, turned over, would just fill up the place left by the preceding flake.

The art of ploughing, perhaps, requires a nicer eye, steadier hands, and more attention than any other occupation; and yet, without fixed principles or rules of any kind, the most ignorant persons are trusted with a plough; although the difference of one man's ploughing and another's shall make the odds of 2 or 3 quarters produce per acre, on the same land: For it is obvious, that land unequally and irregularly ploughed, with flat, shallow, broad flakes, laid over on their backs, never can produce so well as when the furrows are taken deeper, narrower, and shouldered up against each other. By which means, there are more numerous intervals proper to receive the seed; and it is also better covered with the soil, protected from the bleaching rains and scorching heats, and enabled sooner to fulfil the purposes of vegetation.

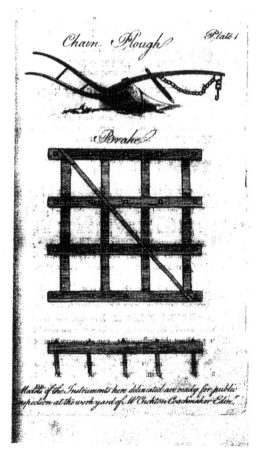

Plate 1 from *The gentleman farmer*[203]

We are, however, extremely inattentive to clean the lands from root–weeds, couch–grass, or quickens;[204] and to destroy the multitude of annuals which continually spring in so wet a soil. Neither do we sufficiently pulverize the land by harrows, brakes, and rollers; without which, the tender germs and seeds can find no proper nidus to call forth their vegetating powers.[205] By attending to these particulars, and clearing the field of all superfluous moisture, by the judicious formation of water furrows to take off the rains and springs; a good ploughman can easily compensate for any additional wages his master can bestow upon him: Insomuch, that it would be better for a farmer to give a skilful Berwick or East–Lothian or Clackmannanshire ploughman, double wages, rather than allow the land to be ploughed gratis in the old Ayrshire form.

The more ordinary farmers still continue the old Scotch plough, which, for breaking up coarse land, and working strong stony soils, is probably the best of all; but it is extremely heavy, and requires four horses. In lighter and well cultivated soils, a smaller plough is used, and works easily with two horses, and without a driver. This mode, it is presumed will very soon become general in the county. The Ayrshire ploughs, however, appear all too narrow in the bottom; by which it is more difficult to keep a straight direction, and to shoulder up the ridge, than with a plough broader at bottom, and bluff at the mouldboard, thereby rendered steady in its progress, although not so proper for strong stoney lands. Double mouldboards are used for drills and green crops, but the wheel ploughs do not prevail in any part of Ayrshire.[o.f.] Several attempts have been made to introduce cast metal ploughs; but they appear much heavier, and in no respect superior to those of wood well shod with iron in the ordinary mode.

A two horse plough, of Mr Small's construction, with an iron head, costs two guineas; with a wooden head, 30s; cast metal ploughs, 40s.[206]

Draining

There is another point of equal consequence in this county to which as yet no adequate attention has been shown. The tenacious nature of the soil in many places, and the moisture of the climate, expose it to constant inconveniences from wetness. The extent of the evil has hitherto almost entirely precluded the application of a remedy. Covered stone drains are so expensive, and in general so ineffectual, they have justly fallen into disrepute.[207] To drain an acre of ground with stones and covered drains will cost from £3 to £5 per acre; and after all, the slightest accident or impediment in any of the drains, will render them entirely useless.

Drains filled with brush–wood are extremely eligible for soft boggy lands, where there is a sufficient declivity communicating with a main drain to carry off the various streamlets from the drains. They do not cost more than 40s or 50s per acre, in the neighbourhood of brush–wood; but they seldom last beyond 14 or 15 years. And if the mouths of the drains are ever suffered to choak, they cease to be of service.

There is another kind of covered drains, less expensive, and in certain soils more efficacious than the former. First, a thick sod is cut and laid aside, then a trench is made gently shelving, and deep enough to be beyond the reach of any plough. A narrower spade is then used to cast a smaller trench at bottom, leaving a shoulder or epaulement of several inches on each side. The earth is then carefully removed, and the top sod is turned with the sward downwards pressing on the epaulement, and leaving the narrow space below it empty for the water. The earth scooped from the bottom is then thrown upon the inverted sod, and the whole is levelled with the surface. Neat as this mode may be for dressing pleasure grounds and parks, it is found inadequate to the great purposes of draining on an extensive scale. In a county such as Ayrshire, this can only be effected by properly ridging and furrowing the land; opening with a spade or plough a proper water furrow, wherever it is necessary; and in wet or spouty soils using open cuts or kettle–bottom drains, about 5 feet wide at top, gently shelving, so as to leave the sides green, and no deeper than is requisite to make the water flow. These kettle–bottom drains may be made from 4d to 6d per fall of six yards, and ought to be cleaned once or twice a year. They have been successfully practised by Mr Blair in very wet parts of his estate.[208]

Ditches and Fences

The only kind of drain that hitherto has been generally established, arises collaterally from the large deep ditches and fences which over–run Ayrshire. When the system of enclosing was introduced, every one conceived that the deeper and wider he made his ditch, and the higher he constructed his mound, the more secure and efficient was his fence. In this course of reasoning, it was forgotten that the mound acted as a barrier against the water on one side, and the ditch as a canal or dam upon the other, whenever there was not a proper level or outlet for the water. The width is usually 5 or 6 feet, and the depth three feet. The thorns are planted on a level with the surface, and usually with a scarcement or projection of 5 or 6 inches; on this the thorns rest, and it serves as an under stratum to them when cleaned, or when earth is thrown to cover them. A fence, of this sort, costs at the rate of 10d or 1s per fall or perch of 6 yards in length. On the top of it, is placed a pallisadoe of brushwood, costing according to situation, from 2d to 4d per fall.

In Summer, this ditch or canal is dry, and so wide that the cattle can descend into the bottom, and destroy the thorns growing above the projecting earth or scarcement. In Winter, the quicks are usually drowned with the stagnated water in the ditch, and although the Ayrshire soil is generally favourable to these plants, so little attention is paid to them, that one may ride for many miles without seeing a hedge and ditch either properly constructed at bottom, cleaned above, cocked and pallisadoed at top, or twitched up like a penthouse, which is the only mode of preserving the fence, thick and vigorous from top to bottom.[209]

Quicks are raised from hips and haws; and after standing in the seed–bed, they are transplanted; and at three years old, are usually sold by the nursery–man at 10s per thousand.[o.f.]

Original footnote: 34 quicks are sufficient to plant a fall of 6 yards.

Considering the enormous sums expended on enclosures in Ayrshire, during the last 40 years, it is wonderful how few are either properly constructed, or afterwards preserved in condition, to perform the three effects required of them: The draining of the ground; the confining and separating of the stock; and affording warmth and shelter to the country. This last object is so material, that an author of great eminence, on political economy, expressly states the signal benefits derived in Italy, from the warmth and shelter of planting and enclosures. If this remark applies with justice to the mild latitudes of Lombardy and Naples; how much more forcibly must it attach to the bleak regions of the north?

Original footnote: Filangieri. Scienza della Legiflazione.[210]

The best mode of attaining these objects is, to construct a mound or embankment, about 3 or 4 feet wide at bottom, and from 2 or 3 feet high, faced up with sod, in order that it may be preserved in constant verdure; with a quickset hedge and row of trees upon the top, defended by pailing or brushwood while the fence is young, and having a small shelving drain on each side of the embankment. The earth being all taken from the surface, and well pulverized, gives much more luxuriant vegetation to the quicks and trees, than can be expected when they are plunged into the side of a cold hard mound, often drenched with water, and placed in an unnatural horizontal posture. It is, however, to be observed, that these fences are by no means proper in very sandy ground, where the drought would kill the plants.[o.f.1] A mound and fence of this description, including thorns at 10s per thousand, and a sufficient quantity of oak, ash, elm, beach,[o.f.2] and larch at the rate of one tree per fall, and one Huntington willow per fall, may be made for little more than an ordinary enclosure.[211] It is particularly beautiful and convenient on the sides of the high roads, affording a perfect fence and some shelter; preserving them dry without recurring to the pernicious custom of deep ditches fronting the road, which endanger the neck of the traveller throughout every part of Ayrshire.

Original footnote 1: In that case, furze, planted on a high mound or turf dyke, will be found an eligible substitute.[212]

Original footnote 2: The beech is above all recommended, and it agrees so well with the thorn, that it may be mingled with it in the hedge.

Roads

With respect to roads, few counties, on the whole, are so well accommodated. In all directions, where land or water gravel can be procured, the roads are formed of these materials. The turnpike roads are made and repaired by the produce of the tolls; and cross roads by the statute labour of the different parishes.[213] The usual breadth is conformably to statutory regulations; being never less than 24 feet wide for by–roads, and 34 feet wide for turnpike roads. The materials are usually a foot deep at the sides, and 15 inches in the centre. When the turnpike roads first began in this county, the rate of making them, by job–work, rose from 10s to 14s per fall. Now, they are contracted for at 5s to 6s per fall; unless where the materials are at a great distance.

In places where gravel cannot be procured, the road is formed with pounded stones; but as they are seldom properly covered with earth, nothing can be more uneasy than the travelling on these sharp and rugged communications; especially in this county, where there are neither broad wheels, nor heavy waggons to reduce these refractory materials. The ingenious Mr Bakewell thinks that roads, instead of rising in the centre, and shelving outwards, should be made like the streets of Naples, high at the side, and tending to a kennel or gutter in the middle.[214]

After all, there is little doubt but the best system of road–making is that practised by the Romans in the Appian and Flaminian ways,[215] and afterwards much improved, and rendered general in France under Sully and Colbert.[216] The system established by these great ministers consisted of a broad pavement in the middle, on which carts and carriages can always draw a greater load than on the gravelly paths on each side, which served for travellers in dry weather.

Amount of Weight drawn–Carts, and other Conveyances

The fact is, that in the neighbourhood of Glasgow, where the roads are neither smooth nor flat, but where they are either paved, or composed of very hard materials, from 20 to 30 cwt. is drawn upon a cart with one horse; whereas, on the flat gravel roads around London, the most powerful teams of four horses hardly ever draw more than 40 cwt. equal to 1000 wt. or half a ton per horse.

In Ayrshire the practice of working with waggons, teams, or drays, has never been established. Even the yoking of two horses in one cart is disapproved of; on this principle, that a single horse in a cart avoids the strains and jerks, which so frequent distress the willing ones, while the others save themselves. Besides, the mode requires much less skill and attention in the driver, who can easily take charge of two horses, and two carts.

The wheels of these carts are usually from 48 to 54 inches in diameter.$^{o.f.}$ The axles are made of iron, although many carters now prefer wooden axles, as being lighter, and shaking the horses less. On the same wheels, occasionally can be placed bodies of long carts for the conveyance of hay and straw. The weights drawn in this county are usually no more than from 10 to 12 cwt. Although the carriers who travel from Ayr to Edinburgh seldom take less than a ton every single horse cart; and the very superior practice, in the neighbourhood of Glasgow, already mentioned sufficiently proves what may he effected. Great, however, is the amendment of the county in this respect. About 40 years ago, the late Lord Cathcart being extremely desirous of improving his estates, ordered a number of carts to be made, and given gratis to his tenants. But they were at that time so little accustomed to these machines, and the roads were so bad, that very few accepted of his Lordship's present.[217]

> Original footnote: A pair of such wheels, made of well seasoned ash, will cost for wood 24s, 12 stone of iron 50s, the body £1. Or for a complete mounted single horse cart, £5. The wheels of carts, round London and in many level parts of France, are seldom less than six feet in diameter. By these means, the centre of the axle is three feet from the ground, and the cart placed on that axle is necessarily raised nearly a foot higher. The objections to these very high wheels are, their weight and severity of pressure going down hill.

Weighing Machines

In order to enforce the most useful improvements in the article of conveyance, and to specify the weights that horses draw, every farmer ought to have a machine capable of weighing two tons, with a platform on which the cart runs; and is weighed in the most expeditious manner. These machines are made by Mr Hutchison at Dalkeith, on an ingenious construction. They are so poised, by counteracting levers under the platform, as to weigh horses, cattle, sheep, &c. with great precision, and without being injured by the movement of the animal. Few inventions are so useful to those who buy and sell live stock; as it enables them to avoid all impositions and altercations with graziers or other dealers, and to know, with very great precision, the value and real condition of the animals they purchase.$^{o.f.}$

> Original footnote: A complete machine of this sort, capable of weighing two tons, costs about £20.

Planting

In addition to the circumstances above specified, there is no operation which tends more to the beauty, comfort, and improvement of the country than planting. In this particular the landholders of Ayrshire have not been inattentive. Two centuries ago, there were very considerable forests in this county. At the time of the Reformation, a forest extended from the vicinity of Ayr to Barnwell, or the Kirk of the Forest, as it was then called, 10 miles eastward. This, and every other of any extent in the county, excepting Dalrymple wood on the river Doon, belonging to the Earl of Cassilis, has been long since destroyed. Insomuch that, 50 years ago, there hardly remained any timber or plantation in the county, excepting the natural woods of oak and birch on the banks of the rivers Stinchar, Girvan, Doon, and Ayr, and clumps of ash and sycamore surrounding almost every farmhouse in the northern division called Cunningham; and many of those in the central and southern districts, Coil and Carrick.

It is to be hoped, that a similar misfortune to the country will not again occur; as Mr Forsyth's discovery and application of a plaister, for preserving and restoring trees, enables every one to obtain new stems, and a most vigorous vegetation, from any root that is not totally decayed.[o.f.] At present, the seat of every gentleman in the county is surrounded with a greater or smaller quantity of planting, proportioned to his inclinations, taste, and means.

Original footnote: See Mr Forsyth's pamphlet on this subject.[218]

Those who wish to beautify or shelter a country, rendered so bleak by the misconduct of their progenitors, found it requisite to plant clumps of one or more acres, and belts of different dimensions, from 20 to 300 feet.

In many places hedge–rows have been introduced, and succeed extremely well. But, in a bleak and hyperborean climate, they must be very frequent, and under the cover of well advanced plantations, before they can yield any solid benefit to the country. Whenever they shall become an established part of the general system, besides affording shelter to the fields, they will in 40 years render an estate worth double the value of the soil, by the timber growing on it, without including the great convenience and absolute necessity of stakes, pailing, and brushwood, afforded from the coppices, and younger growth of the plantations.

In order to effect so desirable a purpose, the best mode practised in this county is to sow, on a well–prepared piece of garden ground, the seed of ash, elm, and sycamore, beechmast, acorns, and cones of larches, pines and fir, according to the quantity of ground intended to be planted. The ordinary proportions requisite to plant an acre are about 2000 deciduous trees, 1500 larches and 1500 Scotch firs.[219] Round the boundary should be planted cuttings of Huntingdon willow, which, in four years gives the shelter and appearance of an advanced plantation; and, in the end, yields a wood of great size, extremely light and tough, and almost as useful for country purposes as the ash. If the ground be hard and moist, it is best to turn it previously with the plough, and then to plant the trees at 3 or 4 years old in the months of February and March. But on dry sandy soils, the Scotch firs and larches should be planted in November or December from the seed–bed at 2 years old. Acorns sown or dibbled, thrive extremely well, unless when rabbits, mice, or hares destroy them.

Contractors in this county will engage to plant 5000 trees per acre at specified ages, and to supply all deficiencies for 7 years at £3 or £4, according to the soil and situation; the proprietor enclosing the ground, and affording some land for nursery. But as most proprietors can do the same much cheaper by their own people, there are few examples of such contracts having been made, to any extent, in the county.

It is unfortunate, that in the early tendency to planting, the landholder should have given so decided a preference to the bleak and dismal Scotch fir. At its prime it never can be used with safety for rafters, beams, joists, or other durable operations in building; insomuch, that the people of this county, rather choose to pay 16d and 18d per square foot for Norway timber, than use the fir grown in Scotland of equal size at 1s per foot.

Large oak, ash, and elm sell for 1s 6d per square foot, beech and sycamore at 1s. Oak bark from £6 to £10 per ton.

With respect to larch, there is not yet a sufficiency of it in the market to ascertain its price; but it is admitted to be worth 3d or 4d per foot more than Scotch fir, grows faster, and is far more beautiful.

The grey willow, although it has the advantage of growing fast and affording early shelter, is so inferior to the Huntington as to render the latter very generally preferred. Several improvers in this county have found great benefit from plantations of hoop and basket willows. The cuttings are planted in the month of March, in rows 3 feet asunder, and the plants 18 inches distant in the rows, on rich meadow land, previously trenched, and ridged up with drains to carry off superfluous water. In three years the shoots are ready for the market; and frequently sell for £24 per acre, yielding a rent of £8 annually, from whence is to be deducted the expense of trenching, planting, and attendance, probably not exceeding £3 per acre.

An excellent kind of reed grows around the lakes and bogs in some parts of this county; and it is to be regretted that the cultivation of this useful plant has not been more encouraged. It affords the best of all thatch, capable of lasting without repair for twenty or thirty years; thereby preventing the consumption of straw, which requires to be almost annually replaced; and, instead of augmenting fodder for the straw–yard, is thus wasted in thatching cottages, and purposes not so necessary, or for which other materials are to be preferred.

Soils and Manures

We come now to the most important point connected with the management of land; the consideration of those qualities which occasion sterility or vegetation, and the applying of such manures as tend to diminish the one, and to promote the other. Without entering into a long technical analysis of the component particles which constitute soil, or the chemical processes through which nature calls forth the principles of vegetation, by the mingling and fermenting of various salts, acids, alkalies and other substances; we may, in general, state the basis of workable soils to consist, either of argillaceous matter, or clay properly so called; or else of flinty earths, quartz, and silicious particles which form the component parts of gravel and sand.*o.f.*

> *Original footnote:* Dr Black ranges earthy substances under 5 classes: 1st, absorbent, or alkaline earths; 2d, clays; 3d, flinty substances; 4th, fusible earths; 5th, talcs or flexible earth.[220]

The various kinds of loams, moulds, mosses, and virgin earths, are formed by the addition of animal or vegetable bodies; such as dung, carrion, decayed wood, leaves, plants, peat, fixed and common air, sediment of water, and other substances conducive to the purposes of vegetation.*o.f.* [221] Alkaline earths, or calcareous matter, acting on the mineral or vegetable acids, produce a great increase of fertility. On the other hand, the intermixture of ores, ochres, copper, iron, and other metallic particles, or waters impregnated with them, tend extremely to diminish the fertility of any soil; and in many instances prove completely fatal to the growth of plants. The famous copper mine of Angelsea, the waters of which destroy all vegetation, may be cited as an example.[222]

> *Original footnote:* The ancient writers on husbandry mention many nostrums for determining the quality of soil.
> A fat black earth is recommended by Virgil as the best for corn:
> "Nigra fere et presso pinguis sub vomera terra et cui putre solum (namque hoc imitamur arando), optima frumentis." Virg. Georg. II, 203–205.*
> In another place, the same author recommends a glutinous soil. A salt or bitter taste was admitted as a testimony of barrenness:
> "Salsa autem tellus et quæ perhibetur amara, frugibus infelix." Virg. Georg. II, 238, 9.†
> Columella says: " Pingue sit. Per se tamen id parum est, si dulcedine caret." Col. II, 2, 18.‡

---

* Generally land that is black and rich under the plough's pressure, and possessing a crumbly soil (for soil like this, we imitate with our ploughing) is best for corn.

† On the other hand, land that is salty, the kind called bitter, is disastrous for crops.

‡ The soil should be rich. Yet that in itself is not sufficient, if it lacks sweetness.

Pliny states that the best soil is known by its smell: "Illa erit optima quæ unguenta sapiet." Plin. Nat. Hist. XVII, 3, 38.*

Although the ancients were ignorant of chemical analysis, yet their opinions on these points deserve the attention of every farmer, and are accurately discussed by the Rev. Mr Dickson, in his work on the Husbandry of the Ancients.[223]

It is well known to chymical observers that not only the muriatic, nitrous, and vitriolic acids are contained in many soils and strata;[o.f.1] but likewise the sorelline and other vegetable acids.[224] These acids, and many other salts, remain either neutralized or combined in such forms as ready to be called forth, by the application of heat and mixture producing combinations which refer to, and are explained by, the table of elective attractions.[o.f.2] Not only the single, but the double elective attractions operate with great force in the processes of nature, in regard to soil, manures, and vegetation.

Original footnote 1: Clay and vitriolic acid form alum.[225] Calcareous earth and vitriolic acid form selenite. The purest clay or argillaceous earth is obtained by adding to a solution of alum, a proportion of magnesia.[226] This decomposes the earth of alum, which is precipitated in the purest form.

Original footnote 2: Single elective attraction means, the disuniting of one body from another by the adjunction of a third. Double elective attraction implies, that when two substances, which have an affinity together, are mixed with two others, these two shall be decomposed, and each shall form a combination with one of the two substances added.

In many parts of America, where the soil is composed, not of sand simply, nor argilla simply, but of these, mingled with rich animal and vegetable substances, full of animal salts and vegetable acids, forming deep moulds and loams; the application of gypsum, or Paris plaister, in the small proportion of a few bushels to an acre, seldom fails to call forth the productive powers of the land, and to ensure abundant crops.[o.f. 227] But if the same quantity of gypsum be spread on mere sand, quartz, till, or clay, unmingled with any animal or vegetable substance, its operation will be of no avail.

Original footnote: The basis of gypsum is, calcareous earth. It is a stoney concretion extremely soft, and does not effervesce with acids. But when reduced into powder, and boiled for some time in a solution of common fixed alkali, it changes into a vitriolated tartar.

---

* That soil will be best which has the savour of perfume.

In like manner, when sal–glauber,[228] which is a neutral salt, produced by the mixture of the vitriolic acid with the fossil alkali,[229] is spread on soil, whose component parts contain particles, brought into action with that preparation, on the principle of chymical attraction; great fertility is the never failing consequence.

Unfortunately, this analyzing mode of operation is repugnant to the habits of practical farmers, and it is only by the application of scientific men, and the attention of such a board as that which I have the honour of addressing, that the necessary investigations can be specified or promulgated. In default of such assistance; under the apprehension, too, of being charged with theoretical deviations from the plain matter in discussion, and in expectation that ere long, by the exertions of so respectable an institution, the public mind will be more fully matured for the reception of chymical deductions applied to agricultural purposes; I shall, in the mean while, confine myself to those ordinary modes of fertilizing admitted into common practice. The spreading of sand on clay, clay on sand; earth on peat, or peat on earth, every farmer understands to be an improvement of the soil. But, in this county, with every variety of soil and opportunity for these processes, there are few instances of such ameliorations to any extent.

Paring and Burning

The paring and burning of moors and mosses, formerly took place to a considerable degree. It tended to produce two good crops, or three; but was extremely pernicious, unless where the soil was very deep, or where the object was to consume the soil, until you reached a better under–stratum.

Flooding and Watering of Ground

Another custom, very prevalent in this county, was, by means of sluices, dams, or other contrivances, to throw bogs and lower grounds under water during the winter months. By these means, the land was greatly enriched with the productive vegetable earth from the surface of the higher parts. The waters were let off in Spring, and the ground was then ploughed and sown. But in consequence of the great humidity and usual deepness of the soil, the crops were very late, the produce was precarious, depending on the dryness of the season; as a wet summer commonly lodged and spoiled the corn on such lands. Whenever these grounds have been perfectly freed from wetness, springs, and surface–water, they have proved themselves the best of all soils. But the least inattention to these particulars, to the proper ridging of the land, opening of drains, and water furrows, exposed them to numerous disadvantages.

The plan of watering fields by little drains, and dams of a few inches wide, in this mode using stagnant water as a manure, so successfully practised in other countries, and in England by Mr Bakewell at Dishley &c.,[230] has never, as far as I know of, been attempted in Ayrshire. Indeed, at first, some portion of the ludicrous would probably attach to an improver who, in a county such as ours, should in this manner attempt to water fields, before he had thought of draining them. Far be it from me, however, to doubt, but this is one of the most efficacious manures, which, under proper modes and circumstances, can possibly be applied to land. In order to give it full effect, nothing more is requisite than to secure a small streamlet, and to conduct it along the highest part of a field, from that feeder forming furrows with the plough, at moderate distances, then throwing in, small dams of turf at proper intervals, so as to flood every part of the field, for the period necessary to enrich it.*o.f.*

> *Original footnote:* In India, and other tropical climates, machines are constructed for conveying water to every well cultivated field.

Marles

In Carrick or the southern district of the county, shell, clay, and stone marle are found in many places, and applied with advantage. One estate in Carrick of 900 or 1000 acres, which about 40 years ago was sold for little more than £2000, and let for about £100 a year, has been so much improved by marle, as now to let for £600 or £700 a year.

Shell marle, containing a larger proportion of calcareous earth, is the strongest and most speedy in its operation. About 100 cart loads of it, on an acre of earthy or clay land, yields large crops, and continues its operation on the soil for many years. The clay marle containing a smaller quantity of calcareous matter, mixed with a larger portion of argillaceous substance, is more applicable to light soils, and requires to be spread, to the amount of 200 or 300 cart loads per acre. The same observations nearly apply to stone marle. The expence in common cases may amount to £2 or £3 per acre; and the usual mode is to spread the marle on the sward, and plough it in, with the lay crop.

Marle and lime are understood to operate as manures, exactly in proportion to the calcareous matter they respectively contain. Many kinds of marle do not contain more than one–twentieth, or even one–thirtieth part of their weight of calcareous earth. Half the quantity of lime would be infinitely preferable to such marles.*o.f.*

> *Original footnote:* In order to ascertain the quantity of calcareous matter in marle, Dr Black recommends to dissolve it in acid, and then precipitate by an alkali. Or as a more simple process, to put 200 grains of the marle in a florence flask, adding a little water; and after saturating with an acid, observing the loss of weight.[231] If it lose 40 grains, there are one hundred grains of calcareous matter in the marle. The loss of weight which it suffers being always about 40 per cent. of the whole, and whatever the loss of weight, we can by this mode judge of the quantity of calcareous matter contained.

Lime

Lime, however, is the staple manure of this county. It has been already stated that 100 bolls, or 400 Winchester bushels, of slacked lime, are commonly spread upon the sod:[232] and if the ground remains for several years in grass, on land of a good strong staple, whether loam or clay, it will make the difference of 4s or 5s per acre on the pasture; raise an abundance of white clover even in the wildest moor, where no such plant had been seen before.

If the ground is ploughed, for 3 years, it will yield several quarters of grain per acre more than would have been produced without the lime. On sandy ground it is not the practice to use lime, although it evidently improves the pasture even of that soil; and on such parts of the moors as are previously drained it produces the very best effects. But when thrown upon land in a deluged condition, little benefit can be derived from the application.

On the coast, the limestone is brought as ballast from Lerne,[233] and other places in Ireland.[o.f.] It costs 3s 6d per ton of stones delivered at the harbour. It is sold from the draw–kilns at 6d per boll of slacked lime, equal to half a boll of shells. A ton of limestone will produce 8 or 9 bolls of slacked lime; and, in addition to the price of 6d per boll, it frequently costs as much to lead it, and lay it on the ground: So that farmers expend £5 per hundred bolls of lime, which is the usual quantity spread upon an acre.

> *Original footnote:* In some parts of Ireland, there is an ingenious contrivance for erecting salt pans over a draw–kiln, so as to perform the operations of each, with the same fire.[234]

Many farmers maintain, that instead of adhering to this expensive practice, of spreading so large a quantity of lime per acre on the sward, it is better to spread the half upon a fallow. This is daily coming into use, when land is preparing for wheat or barley, to which 40 or 50 cart–loads of dung per acre are added when they be spared. Failing dung, a compost made of lime and sweepings of drains and ditches, is found to produce the most luxuriant crop of grain; and acts as an admirable top–dressing for hay and pasture lands.

It is asserted by some improvers, that the burning of the lime, and the caustic quality it thereby acquires, are not requisite to call forth its ameliorating powers; being, as they say, equally efficient when merely pulverized, without burning and spread in powder. Dr Black, indeed, positively maintains, that lime is equally applicable in its mild, as in its caustic state;[o.f.] that it should remain 12 months on the sward before the ground be ploughed, by which it sinks into the earth, is incorporated with the soil, and corrupts the vegetable matter, so forming a manure.

> *Original footnote:* See Dr Black's Lectures.[235]

It is an opinion very prevalent in Ayrshire, that although lime improves the land, and enables it to produce superior crops of grass and corn; yet that, if repeated, it exhausts the soil, and would at last reduce it to a caput mortuum. It is obvious, that if a farmer, whether by lime or any other means, can bring his fields into high condition, either he or his landlord must be culpable indeed, if they be afterwards reduced to barrenness. But, perhaps, the operation of lime being to attract and bring into action the different acids contained in the ground, may leave the soil diminished in its means of reproducing these ingredients; without which, when the operation of liming is repeated, the calcareous matter may remain inactive and without effect.

Peat or Moss

It is to be regretted, that so few endeavours have been made in this county, to render peat or moss, productive as a manure. Every chemical person knows that peat or moss contains a proportion of vegetable matter; that the vegetable alkaline salts are obtained from it by burning; and that the application of alkaline matter may be used to call forth the sorelline and other acids which abound in it. The few attempts which have been made in this respect, encourage us to persist in more vigorous endeavours, and the extreme plenty and cheapness of the material, render the application of it as a manure one of the greatest desiderata in Scottish husbandry.

Common Salt

The learned and ingenious Bishop of Landaff[236] states, that common sea salt, as a manure, in small quantities, tends to fertilize, whereas, in large proportions, it effectually destroys vegetation. Perhaps in this latter mode of application, it might be useful to destroy the roots of quickens, rushes, and other pernicious weeds, which infect this county.

Soapers Waste

Soapers waste, which is the earthy part of kelp and barilla,[237] mixed with the lime which manufacturers use to bring it to the caustic state, and from which the alkaline and other salts have been separated by solution, proves a valuable manure, and is in great request among many Ayrshire farmers, as well as horn shavings, for the purpose of spreading upon grass.

Sea-weed

Sea-weed is much used upon the coast. It is sometimes carried immediately from the water, and ploughed in, for barley or other crops. But is more frequently allowed to rot; and in that state is spread at the rate of 70 or 80 single horse-carts per acre. It does not however seem to continue its effects above two succeeding crops, especially in sandy soils; although in clay lands it is more durable. When used for turnip, it is apt to burn and destroy the seed; insomuch, that unless carefully managed, it will often occasion a failure of the crop, on the same field where the part manured with dung, proves luxuriant. It is likewise observed to give an unpleasant taste to potatoes, and some other vegetables.

Dung

With respect to dung, any observations on its value or mode of action would be superfluous. It only remains to express regret, that so little pains are taken in this county to increase its quantity, and preserve it in a proper state. Instead of forming layers of alternate mould and dung, and turning it at proper intervals, the lower and more ignorant class of farmers, still continue the barbarous practice of throwing it out from the stable or cow–house on a declivity, where its juices are exhausted, or run off with the rain which drenches it. The benefits arising from feeding all the live stock in stables, sheds, or straw–yards, as practised in the Netherlands, are however, so well understood, at least in theory, throughout this county, that they cannot fail ere long to be very generally established.

The ploughing in of vetches, tares, lupines, or other pulse, when green, is also recommended as an excellent manure by the best rustic writers; but if allowed to form the seed, they have at all times been held pernicious.

Stock

So much respecting the nature and management of land in Ayrshire. The next object is to consider the kinds and properties of those animals which are maintained on its productions.

The prejudices long entertained in this country against the use of pork or bacon, prevented the inhabitants from paying due attention, to the breed of swine. But the merits of this useful animal are now recognised, and its flesh rises in estimation among all classes of the people. Although many farmers keep a few for their own use, yet they are seldom raised or fed in any considerable numbers, unless at gentlemen's houses (where the small, round, black, Chinese kind, are generally preferred), or at distilleries, where the superior size and weight of the large, white, Shropshire hogs, render them more eligible for the market.

The ass has also fallen under the displeasure of the Ayrshire people, so that there is hardly a quadruped of this description to be seen.

Mules

An attempt was made some years ago, by the late Mr Oswald, to introduce mules.[238] With this view, he procured, at great expense, remarkable fine jack–asses from Spain, and bred a number of excellent, well–sized mules, at his seat of Auchincruive.

Some of these were sold in the county, but notwithstanding their durability and hardiness, there is scarcely one of them now. And the farmers all prefer horses, which for draught and farming work, are perhaps, superior in this county to any in the kingdom.

Horses

The Ayrshire horses are neither flat footed, gummy legged, clumsy animals, like the unwieldy breed, which supplies the drays of London; nor are they by any means so slight and flimsy, as the working stock of Yorkshire. On the contrary, they are short and active on their legs, hard in the hoofs, large in the arms, very deep and powerful in the counter, straight in the back, square in the body, and broad across the fillets. Their predominant defects are, a shortness and coarseness of the forehand, and a deficiency of that elegance of form and action, which only belong to particular descriptions of high–bred, or foreign horses. Formerly, the black and grey colours used to prevail; but of late years, a decided preference has been given to the bays and browns, with black tails, legs, and manes. These have been improved by strong chapman stallions, covering from different parts of England.[o.f.]

> *Original footnote:* Chapman stallions, are those which cover at the different fairs and markets, for coach and saddle stock; being neither thorough bred, like racers, nor so coarse as the dray, and waggon breed.

It is generally believed, that the valuable, hardy breed of strong work horses, so remarkable in this, and the adjoining county of Lanark, had been chiefly owing to some Flanders or Holstein stallions, brought over last century by one of the Dukes of Hamilton. But it appears from the works of Fordun,[239] Pitscottie,[240] Æneas Sylvius,[241] Froissard,[242] the Epistolæ Regum Scotorum,[243] and other compositions on Scottish affairs, that great pains had been taken, at early periods, under several of the Scottish Kings, particularly during the reigns of King David Bruce, and all the James's, to bring, not only active breeds for the saddle from Hungary, Spain, and Barbary, but also to import strong and useful kinds from Flanders, Germany, and Denmark.[o.f 1,2.]

> *Original footnote 1:* Any one desirous of knowing the state of stock and agriculture in ancient times, may consult the statute of Alexander II anno 1214, containing instructions regulating the stocking of farms and husbandry. At that period, all the ploughing was performed by oxen.

> *Original footnote 2:* This may help to account for the value of the prevailing race in question; as the strong black breed of Leicestershire, is understood to have originated from an introduction of Flanders horses into that county, by a Lord Hastings, several centuries ago. Every one acquainted with the history of animals, knows, that in five generations, any cross breed, may be brought, to the properties of the original dam or sire: In

the same manner as the descendants of a mulatto, are brought to be perfectly white or completely black in the course of the same number of gradations. This fact explains the rapidity, with which any favourite breed of animals may be introduced into a country.

Few stallions in Ayrshire cover for more than 10s or 15s, but great attention is paid to movements, colour, strength, and form. The grass is so late in this county, that many farmers do not wish their mares to foal till near the end of May; especially as their producing sooner, interferes with the barley seed time, and prevents their being used at that busy period. The foal is allowed to suck 5 or 6 months, during which time, the mare is only used at gentle work. Suckers at weaning time, sell from £7 to £12; yearlings and two–year–olds from £12 to £20. And it is by no means uncommon to pay £30, and £40 for a work–horse or strong breeding mare. Ordinary farming work, however, is performed by horses worth about £20; and multitudes of low priced, light carcassed horses, are annually brought from Ireland, to the fairs at Ayr, Irvine, and Kilmarnock.

A few racing stallions of high pedigrees have covered in the county, and produced a breed extremely different from the farming stock I have endeavoured to describe.[o.f.]

> *Original footnote:* In order as much as possible to improve the breed of horses, already so excellent in the county, it has been my object, to procure the strongest Flanders stallion, of a bay colour, and of that sort which bring their legs well under them, and are speedy in their movements. He weighs above 1200 weight, walks fast, and trots at the rate of 13 miles in the hour, being able to draw 2 tons. A proper selection of the best breed of bay Flanders mares, would be a valuable acquisition; but they are difficult to be procured. It has also appeared to me no less necessary, to introduce the strongest thorough bred stallion that can be found, for the purpose of producing, with proper crosses, horses possessing vigour, power, and action, fit for cavalry, or carriage, or for the field.

It is to be observed that all thorough bred horses are derived from Barbs or Arabs, without any other mixture.[o.f.] These have been introduced and propagated with great expense and care, since the days of Charles the II. And as most of the fine stallions in the kingdom, are either entirely, or in part, of this Arab breed, it unavoidably tends to diffuse throughout the general race of horses, the properties and defects attached to this description of animals. Now, although the Barbs and Arabs are superior to others for speed and endurance of exertion, yet they have many imperfections, which, unless corrected by crossing them with other breeds, render them inapplicable to various important purposes.

> *Original footnote:* Even those who cover under the denomination of chapman stallions, are commonly half or three–quarters bred.

They are in general unfit for draught, owing to the delicacy of their frame, and their physical deficiency of weight. Few thorough bred horses weighing more than 800 lb. They are generally thin in the quarters, small in the limbs, tender in the hoofs, and are apt to go near the ground, which, with their slender forehands, and incapacity of moving with the quick turns, evolutions, and conversions of the Turkish or Hungarian horses, render them neither useful as cavalry, safe for the road, nor elegant in harness.

You will forgive me, Sir, for this digression suggested by the prevailing tendency of reducing all kinds of horses, too near the standard of the racer. While, in my apprehension, the public utility would be more successfully promoted, by propagating only the most powerful of the Arab race, so as to intermix the valuable qualities of that breed, with the weight, hardiness, and modes of action belonging to other kinds, and necessary for the different purposes in which horses are employed.^{o.f.}

> *Original footnote:* The most active and beautiful parade horses in Europe are the Neapolitan. And the horses of Curdistan, are, in many respects, superior to the Arab, being hardier, and of a firmer texture in the hoof, lifting their feet higher, less apt to stumble; of great speed, and accustomed to a rocky country. It may perhaps, be thought fanciful to hint, that in the opinion of many nations, the flesh of horses is not less salutary and wholesome, and equally well tasted as that of oxen. It is eaten by all the race of Tartars, and several other tribes of people, and if their example were to be adopted in other countries, the horse would become, in every respect, an animal more useful, and as economical as the ox.

Neat Cattle

With respect to neat cattle, the necessity of doing much in little time, in order to take advantage of a favourable interval, to make up for the interruption of labour, occasioned by bad seasons, has led to the total disuse of oxen, for the purposes of farming in this county; especially as their feet are seldom found to stand work on hard roads. It is, however, an admitted fact, that the cattle of India, Italy, Portugal, and many other parts of the world, perform all kinds of labour, and are constantly used both in farming and on the road, without suffering any inconvenience.^{o.f.}

> *Original footnote:* All the artillery in India is drawn by oxen. But they are finer in the limbs, harder in the hoofs, and less heavy in the carcase,

than the breed of this kingdom, partaking, in a great measure, of the Beson race described by Buffon and other naturalists.[244]

So far are the oxen, even of this country, from being slow or awkward in their movements, when properly attended to, that the writer of these sheets trained a pair of them which ploughed without a driver, and tilled about an English acre daily.

In treating of Ayrshire cattle, however, we are only to consider them as used for fattening or for dairies. Throughout the greatest part of Carrick, or the southern district of the county, the Galloway breed prevails. These, by great pains and long attention, have been brought to high perfection, and, in many particulars, are preferable for fattening, to any breed in either kingdom. They are generally black or brindled, though some of them are white or dun, and the best breed of them are polled.[o.f.1] [245] They are short legged, rough haired, long bodied, deep in the chest, full in the carcase, and round across the hips and sirloin. They commonly weigh from 20 to 40 stone English, are very hardy, easily fed, often produce one fourth of their weight in tallow, and grow fat where the large heavy breed of other counties would be starved.[o.f.2]

> *Original footnote 1:* Several gentlemen have now raised the Galloway breed to a much larger size. Beef commonly sells from 3d to 4d per English pound, and tallow one third dearer.

> *Original footnote 2:* In order to prevent the danger arising from horned cattle in studs and straw yards, the best mode is to cut out the budding knob, or root of the horn, while the calf is very young. This was suggested to me by Mr Robert Burns, whose general talents are no less conspicuous, than the poetic powers, which have done so much honour to the county where he was born.

Great droves of them are annually sent to England at three and four years old, and yield from £5 to £10 a head; and their beef is universally admitted to be excellent.

They are supposed to be as ill adapted as the Lancashire and Leicestershire breed, for the purposes of milk; insomuch, that there is hardly a dairy in the parts of the country where they predominate. But many circumstances lead me to conclude, that this deficiency arises from inattention to milk as an object, any farther than what is necessary to maintain the calf. For, among this breed, many cows are found which yield great quantities of milk, and from which, in dairy countries, would be propagated, kinds, possessing that quality. Whereas, in breeding countries, a cow is only valued in proportion, as she appears adapted, to the purposes of fattening.[o.f.]

Original footnote: The sale of these cattle has, for many years, been of great extent; and a gentleman of this county, by continuing long to purchase large numbers for the English market, acquired a landed property worth from £5000 to £6000 a year.

In Cunningham, or the northern division of the county, a breed of cattle has for more than a century been established, remarkable for the quantity and quality of their milk in proportion to their size. They have long been denominated the Dunlop breed, from the ancient family of that name, or the parish where the breed was first brought to perfection, and where there still continues a greater attention to milk cows and dairies than in any other part of Scotland.[246]

The cattle in this district appear originally to have been of the old Scotch low country kind. Formerly black or brown, with white or flecked faces, and white streaks along their backs, were prevailing colours. But within these twenty years, brown and white mottled cattle are so generally preferred, as to bring a larger price than others of equal size and shape, if differently marked. It appears, however, that this mottled breed is of different origin from the former stock, and the rapidity with which they have been diffused over a great extent of country, to the almost entire exclusion of the preceding race, is a singular circumstance in the history of breeding. Indeed, it is asserted by a gentleman of great skill and long experience,[o.f.] that this breed was introduced into Ayrshire by the present Earl of Marchmont, and afterwards reared at the seat of the Earl of Glasgow, from whence they are said to have spread over all the county.[247]

Original footnote: Mr Bruce Campbell.[248]

This breed is short in the leg, finely shaped in the head and neck, with small horns, not wide, but tapering to the point. They are neither so thin coated as the Dutch, nor so thick and rough hided as the Lancashire cattle. They are deep in the body, but not so long, nor so full and ample, in the carcase and hind quarters as some other kinds. They usually weigh from 20 to 40 English stone, and sell from £7 to £12 according to their size, shape, and qualities. It is not uncommon for these small cows to give from 24 to 34 English quarts of milk daily, during the summer months, while some of them will give as far as 40 quarts, and yield 8 or 9 English pounds of butter weekly. The breed is now so generally diffused, over Cunningham and Coil, that very few of the other sorts, are reared on any well regulated farm. The farmers reckon that a cow yielding 20 quarts of milk per day during the summer season, will produce cheese and butter worth about £6 per annum.

Cheese

The sweetmilk cheese, as it is called, which is the kind generally manufactured in these parts of Ayrshire, is made by curdling each days milk of the dairy separately. After the curd is mixed with salt, and broken with the hand, or cut in shreds, it is pressed extremely hard in a frame, under a stone, moving with a double screw, and often weighing half a ton. The cloth is frequently changed, and in a few days the cheese is taken out of the frame and laid up to dry. It is of a mild and pleasant taste, and sells at an average from 2½d to 4d per English pound, while butter sells from 6d to 7d for the same weight.[249]

It is remarked that the best of these milch cows are good feeders, and easily fattened, although their shapes in several points are different from those approved by Connoisseurs. It appears, indeed, that the qualities of yielding large quantities of rich milk, and of fattening with facility, on a moderate portion of food, are by no means incompatible. And that the reason of those desiderata being seldom united in the same animal, arises rather from the different views with which stock is bred, and the inattention of farmers to the double objects in question, than to any great difficulty, in correcting the shape of the best milch cattle, and rendering them equal in form and aptitude of fattening, to the most approved breeding stock.[o.f.]

> *Original footnote:* Under this impression I have collected some of the favourite kinds of Darlington or Teeswater, and Yorkshire, meaning to cross them with the Ayrshire stock, in order to unite the properties already mentioned.

It is to be observed that several gentlemen in the county, as well as myself, endeavoured, some years ago, to introduce the best breed of the wide horned Craven, Lancashire and Leicestershire cattle. Many of the calves were dispersed among the farmers both in Coil and Cunninghame. But so great is the prejudice against them, that though they were admitted to be very handsome, not one is now remaining in the county.

In former times a proportion of Dutch or Holderness cattle had been propagated, and when well fed, yielded large quantities of milk. But they were thin haired, lank in the quarters, and delicate in the constitution, which rendered them unfit for a soil and climate such as Ayrshire. They were, besides, extremely difficult to fatten, yielded little tallow; and from the spareness of their shapes, incapable of carrying much flesh upon the proper places.

Alderneys and Guernseys have also been occasionally introduced, in order to give a richness and colour to the milk and butter; which they do in a degree superior to any other animal of the cow species.

Graziers are sometimes tempted by the comparative lowness of price to purchase Irish cattle, which are large, wide horned, and raw boned. But they are so difficult to fatten, that they commonly sell £2 or £3 a–head, cheaper than Ayrshire cattle, of the same size and weight.

Other farmers stock their pasture lands with a small breed of Highland cattle, which, at 2 or 3 years old, may be bought from 20s to £3 a–head. These having been bred on hills, and barren heaths, improve most rapidly in the low country. And when fed a year or two on rich pasture, are esteemed superior for taste and flavour to any meat that comes to market.

Sheep

On the subject of animals, it only remains to offer some observations respecting the kinds of sheep in this county. On the dry lands along the coast, a small white faced race has long existed. The little wool they have, is not altogether coarse; but they are loose made, ill shaped, and have no good quality to recommend them. There, is, however, a sort on the estate of Mr Kennedy of Dunure, on the coast of Carrick, whose wool is very fine, and who partake of the properties of the Mochrum or coast–breed of Galloway.[250]

The established Aborigines are bred in great numbers on the moors. They are reckoned by some the most hardy, active, and restless animals of the sheep tribe.[o.f.1] They are round, firm, and well–shaped; black–faced, and black–legged, with large horns. Their wool is open, sharp pointed, and of the coarsest quality; seldom weighs more than 2 or 3lbs per fleece, and not worth 6d for an English pound. The weathers of this sort, are usually bought, at 3 years old, for £10 or £12 per score, and will feed to double that value; weighing about 12 or 15 English pounds per quarter; yielding tallow, equal to one fourth of their weight; and when fed till 5 years old, afford the finest mutton in the kingdom.[o.f.2 251]

Original footnote 1: Others assert, that what is called the long or Cheviot breed, from the closeness of their fleece, can as well, and, some say, can better, resist the inclemency of the seasons.

Original footnote 2: Mutton sell from 3d to 4d per English pound, and tallow one third dearer.

The moorland shepherds are extremely diligent and skilful, taking constant notice of their flocks, and attending to the disorders which frequently afflict them. But in the low parts of the county, great ignorance and inattention on this subject are united. Numbers of sheep perish under the rot and scab. Farmers often lose their cattle by the moor–ill and murrain; and hundreds of horses die every year by botts, grease, strangles, and inflammation of the intestines.[252] It is strange, indeed, that so little attention should be paid to the diseases of animals in this county; that there should neither be persons skilful in the cure of them, nor books and publications circulated to direct the farmer how to act when such disasters happen to his stock.

If it were possible, by any intermixture, to give these animals a less restless nature, and an ample fleece of finer wool, without impairing the hardiness and other qualities which fit them so peculiarly for their bleak and barren situations, it would prove the greatest benefit that could be conferred on moorland property. The heavy, coarse, and long–wooled lazy breeds of Lincoln, Leicester, and Teeswater, could hardly find subsistence under such exposure; and the fine–woolled race of Hereford would probably cease to be distinguished for their carding staple, if drenched in those cold moorland bogs and marshes.[o.f.]

> Original footnote: The Hereford seem, in many of their features, to mark a descent from the fine–woolled Spanish breed, which we know was brought into England, at early periods of our history.

To cross them with the finer and more delicate race of Spain would seem too violent a transition; and the mountain–breeds, in other parts of this kingdom, are in few respects superior to themselves. The Cheviot sheep, indeed, are finer woolled, but their fleeces are by no means equal in value to the Hereford or the Spanish, and they are, in general, of a long–shape, rather loose texture, inferior in these important particulars to the breed we are describing.[o.f.]

> Original footnote: In October last, having occasion to attend a sale of several hundred sheep of various kinds and countries, belonging to the British Wool Society, it appeared to me, that the handsomest sheep exposed was a moorland ram, bought for 12s.[253]

The kind of sheep which I brought from Colchis or Trebisonde, some years ago, being from a cold bleak climate, hardy in their nature, and covered with the finest wool of the long combing kind, afforded great expectations of an admirable intermixture: But in this belief I found myself mistaken.[254]

It is extremely probable, that animals, like plants, may by degrees be reconciled to climates, the most distant from their natural positions. And, as cherries were brought from Pontus, and peaches from Persia, first to Italy, and afterwards, by slow gradations, to France and England; so the finest sheep of Spain, and the silken–fleeced breed of Angora or Ancyra, may in time assimilate with the coldest moors of Ayrshire.[255]

But, for the present, confining our suggestions to such experiments as are within the reach of ordinary farmers; it appears, that the hardiest and most active breed of sheep, producing a valuable coat of wool, whether of the carding or the combing staple, would be the most eligible means of adding to the value of the present moorland race.

With all their disadvantages, it is still a question whether the most chosen kinds of Leicester, Lincoln, Teeswater, or Northumberland, on a specified surface, will produce an equal profit?

It is taken for granted, that the principles established on this subject by the ingenious Mr Bakewell, are correct; and that a sheep, whose bones are small, whose stomach is less capacious, in proportion to his size, and who from habit, disposition, or constitution, has an aptitude to fatten on a more moderate proportion of food, is more valuable than one of opposite tendencies. It still remains to be considered, whether a moorland black–faced wether, weighing 15lbs per quarter, besides a quantity of tallow equal to one fourth of his whole weight, and worth 10s, of whom 5 or 6 may be fattened to double that value, on an acre of land worth 20s, is not a more profitable bargain, than the best Leicester wether, at the ordinary price of 30s. Such a sheep, commonly weighs about 30lbs a quarter, produces a coarse fleece, little tallow, and bad mutton. He is accustomed to feed at the rate of 3 or 4 upon an acre of land, let at 50s or £3. He is unable and unwilling to seek his food at any distance, and is pampered from lambing–time, with hay, oats, and pounded oil–cakes, placed in moveable racks and mangers, under sheds and penthouses, for his accommodation. After all, he does not yield more than 40s or at the utmost, 50s in his fattest state. It is also asserted, that this breed is subject to the rot, and other disorders, which render them unfit to be kept to a proper age, on the strong, wet pastures of Ayrshire. The practice in England being to kill, about 2 years old, all those that are not meant for breeding stock.

Notwithstanding these remarks, it has always appeared to me an eligible object of experiment, to introduce the best breeds of those counties. Various gentlemen in former times had procured a very large race of long–legged sheep from Teeswater and other parts. These, though ill–shaped, and requiring great attention, yielded from 12 to 24 English pounds of wool per fleece; the maximum of which is probably as great a quantity, as is produced at present on any sheep in England. This race blending with the common classes of the country, supplied the farmers with the pets, or tame sheep which were regularly housed and pastured with the milch cows. But there was no regular stock, or considerable number of them, to be found in any part of Ayrshire.[o.f.]

> *Original footnote:* The old Teeswater breed is now so crossed with the Leicestershire, and other kinds, as to have lost its distinctive properties. It used to yield a larger fleece than any sheep in England, probably not even excepting the best breed of Lincolnshire. It seems strange, that, in estimating the value of this useful animal, such exclusive attention should, among the breeders, be now bestowed on carcase, to the almost total disregard of wool.

In the year 1776, several gentlemen of the county, procured six score of ewes, and the use of two rams, from Mr Culley in Northumberland, who charged us what seemed an extravagant price, and supplied us with an indifferent stock.[256] The neighbouring gentlemen in general maintained, that the introduction of this breed would impair the quality of Ayrshire mutton; the farmers asserted, they could not thrive on our wet land and rainy climate; while the manufacturers declared their wool too coarse to be deserving of encouragement.

This breed, however, has increased in favour and in population. They yield in general two lambs from every breeding ewe; weigh about 20 English pounds per quarter, and sell for 25s or 30s at two years old when fat. Yield 8 or 9 lbs. of wool, worth 10d per English lb. And are not only easily maintained on tolerable land, but so quiet, as to remain within the slightest fence; and so much esteemed, that farmers willingly pay 10s or 12s annually, for grazing a breeding ewe of this description. In addition to this kind, I have procured the best breed from Teeswater, and a valuable stock from Mr Bakewell, besides a Spanish ram, together with some Spanish and Hereford ewes, from the British Wool Society. In doing this, it is my object to combine, by different crosses, the best properties of shape and carcase, with the greatest hardiness and aptitude to fatten, as well as the best fleeces of carding and of combing wool. For undoubtedly, it is the duty of landholders, not only to promote, and to diffuse as much as possible, every species of improvement, but to counteract the disgraceful spirit of illiberal monopoly, which has hitherto confined the favourite breeds of useful animals within a narrow range.

Mode of introducing Improvement

This diffusive operation, however, can hardly be effected without the unremitting endeavours of a number of individuals, in their different districts. These require the aid and intervention of public, and associated bodies of men, granting due encouragement and rewards to those who dedicate their skill, and labour, to the amelioration of stock, although their object may have been merely personal emolument, undirected by any public principle.

It is obvious, that instead of one or two fine stallions, bulls, or rams in a whole country, let out at exorbitant rates, every district, nay, every parish, ought to be supplied with these useful means of reproduction on the most moderate terms. With this object, numerous societies of landholders and farmers ought to be established. They should procure the best publications on subjects of agriculture, offering premiums for the finest stallions, bulls, and rams, produced within the parish; advertising annual ploughing matches, granting rewards to the most skilful, and purchasing models, or at least designs of useful implements of husbandry on approved principles, for the instruction of all persons connected with mechanic trades.

If these endeavours were encouraged, and extended by the freeholders at head–courts, and other county meetings, specifying the objects to which, improvements ought in different districts to be directed; they could not fail to be productive of permanent advantage, to the landed interest, and to the community at large.

These remarks, however, have a more immediate reference to the general means that ought to be adopted, for diffusing useful knowledge, and to the institutions necessary for promoting, a regulated system of experiment and improvement, connected with the various branches of rural economy. In China, it is esteemed the proudest distinction of the Emperor, that he is the first cultivator in his own dominions; and it is fortunate for this country, that the attention of the Sovereign, and of his Majesty's government, are graciously bestowed upon an object so deserving of the Royal care.[o.f.]

Original footnote: Don Juan Enrique de Graeff, a Spanish author, in his Discursos Mercuriales, improving on the suggestions of Reaumur, has urged the great national advantages, that might be derived from establishments formed for the purpose of conducting, a connected series of inductions on the kinds, combinations, mixtures, and history of different useful animals.[257]

Although no public institution of this description exists in Great Britain, yet an individual (Mr John Hunter), who, unfortunately for science, is now no more, guided by the impulse of a vigorous and enlightened mind, has extended the bounds of knowledge in this respect, with a successful energy, deserving the sanction and encouragement of a great nation. Especially, when it is considered, that nothing but permanent establishments, and a prolonged course of well–directed observations, can give full effect to the object in view.[258]

These ideas, are, in a great measure confirmed by the benefits which have resulted from similar institutions, connected with the vegetable kingdom. To the Royal and botanical gardens, the public is indebted for much important information. On the President of the Royal Society, Sir Joseph Banks, the best tribute of applause and admiration has been bestowed, by all Europe, for the superior exertions he has made in this extensive range.[259] From the labours of such men, when directed to objects of cultivation, the most luminous discoveries, and useful improvements may rationally be expected.

It is well known, that the most beneficial introduction of plants and animals from one kingdom to another, has arisen from institutions and exertions, such as those to which I have alluded. It would be tedious to enumerate all the esculent plants in Great Britain, which have been brought from other countries; mulberries, and silk–worms from the East, to the Morea, and afterwards to Italy and France; coffee trees, bread–fruit trees, various kinds of cotton shrubs, and other valuable productions, transplanted from one quarter of the globe to another.[260] Neither is it necessary to specify the collections of the Dutch East India Company, in their botanical establishment, at the Cape of Good Hope;[261] those of Mr de Visme, in his celebrated gardens at Lisbon;[262] or the very interesting experiments conducted by Dr Anderson, under the government of Fort St. George,[263] although they probably, are as conducive to the objects in question, as any others on the globe.

One fact is certain, that through negligence and inattention, we lose the benefit of many productions, which might easily be brought to assimilate with our soil and climate.[o.f.]

> *Original footnote:* As instances, we may venture to suggest the luxuriant grass, or broad–leaved gramen of Madagascar, called Fatak, and the hardy kind of rice, which grows on the hills of Cochin–China, without any other water than accidental showers.[264]

It is also proved, that a multitude of plants, which the antients cultivated, for food and other purposes, have totally disappeared from the regimen of modern nations. Among many others, we may mention ervum, ocymum, and in particular cytisus, which was held in such repute among the Romans for feeding every kind of stock.[o.f. 265]

> *Original footnote:* It is surprising that cytisus should have fallen into disuse; for, it was not only reckoned the most profitable, but the hardiest of plants, enduring bad soil, heat, or cold, frost, or snow, without detriment.
>
> From Pliny's account, it appears to have been originally brought from the Cyclade islands, and not to have been very common in Italy; but so productive, that the value of 2000 sesteriæ or £64 was frequently raised upon a jugerum, which was little more than half a Scotch acre.
>
> It may either says Pliny, be cast into the ground with barley, or be sown in spring like leeks, or its shoots may be planted out before winter, about a cubit in length, in furrows one foot asunder. ("Plantæ cubitales seruntur scrobe pedali."*)
>
> It comes to perfection in three years, and begins to be cropped at the vernal equinox, when it ceases to flower; affording green feeding 8 months in the year, and afterwards may be used dry. It is hoary in appearance, and is a shrub, with a narrow trefoil leaf. Columella, after describing its many valuable qualities, for producing milk, fattening cattle, healing their complaints, and affording green forage 8 months in the year, adds: "Præterea, in quolibet agro quamvis macerrimo celeriter comprehendit; omnem iniuriam sine noxa patitur." Col. V, 12, 1.†

---

* When the plants are eighteen inches high, they are transplanted into a trench a foot deep. (Plin. Nat. Hist. XIII, 132, 4.)

† Furthermore on any ground whatsoever, no matter how impoverished, it quickly takes root; and endures any ill–treatment without suffering damage.

It seems, however, like the Lote tree, or Lotometra and Nymphea frutex of Egypt, as well as other valuable plants, to be entirely lost in modern practice.[266]

The Romans were also in the use of feeding their cattle on mast, acorns, lupines, leaves of oak, ash, elm, beech, and poplar.

Observations on Landlords and Tenants—Labourers—Consumers—Manufacturers—and Innovators

We now proceed, to the concluding article of this discussion; to the state and condition of those classes, affected by the cultivation of the country, in the different relations, which the natural order of things establishes, between proprietors, occupiers, and labourers, with those who consume the produce of the soil.

In all transactions, between the landholders and tenants, there is a double and counteracting influence. The relation which they have, as proprietor and occupier of the same ground, unites them by the strongest ties of interest, against the consumer, from whom it is their mutual object to extort the highest price, for every article of produce. They are generally not less accordant against those dangerous innovators, who, in the wantonness of undeserved prosperity, are apt to spring forth among the mercantile and manufacturing classes; maintaining doctrines subversive of the established orders of society; menacing the country with desperate Agrarian systems, tending to destroy the sacred rights of property, and every species of security; and under false pretexts of equal distribution, sounding the tocsin of anarchy and confusion.

It must be confessed, however, that this observation concerning the constitutional sentiments, of the farming interest, is liable to great exceptions. In the vicinity of some towns, where the notions of manufacturers predominate, the farmers have been so far perverted, as to form associations binding themselves under severe penalties, never to offer any mark of civility, to any person in the character of a gentleman. The consequences are, that they become boorish and brutal to every individual of the human species, and savage to the brute creation. These outrageous manners are considerably increased, by the harshness and austerity, which characterise different sectaries, who abound in this county.

Whenever this degrading tendency prevails, it becomes the duty of all persons, connected with property in land, to form counter–associations, binding themselves never to grant leases to persons of such a description; and, at all events, till this malady subsides, to grant no leases, but from year to year, and to tenants at will.

In all engagements between the landlord and his tenants, touching land, their interests, to a certain degree, are discordant. It is naturally the proprietor's object, to gain as much rent, and to lay out as little money on the farm as possible.

On the other hand, the tenant has a direct interest, in throwing the whole burden of improvement upon the landlord; and in giving the smallest possible return.

It is besides the constant object of the landlord, to prevent the land from being over–cropped, neglected, or exhausted; while, at the end of every lease, the tenant has the strongest temptation to crop the land as much us it can bear. He does this not only for immediate profit, but in order to render the farm less valuable, and consequently, to obtain a renewal of his lease on cheaper terms.

This sufficiently refutes an opinion, entertained by some enlightened men, that a principle laid down by Dr Smith, that Government ought not to interfere, by its regulations and restrictions, in the concerns of individuals, applies to the transactions between tenant and proprietors.[267] The landlord who acts on this idea, and neglects to insert judicious covenants in his leases, will find his land exhausted, and his estate impaired; while those who fancy that the skill and information arising from the habits of ordinary farmers, render them either safe to be entrusted with unlimited powers of management, or likely to invent new modes of operation, are contradicted by the fact. For, in this country, improvements have in general been established, not by the farmers, who can ill afford such speculations; but, as they ought to be, at the expense and hazard of the landholder.

On this principle, farmers should not only be restrained from over–ploughing and mismanagement, but the course and rotation should be specified; engaging them by covenant, to sow grass seeds, to drill beans, to fallow for turnips, vetches, kail, or colewort, rape, and cabbages; to hurdle sheep on light land, to construct straw–yards, feed with oil–cakes, and erect sheds or hovels for their outlying stock; above all, never to have more than one, or at the utmost two succeeding crops of corn on the same field, without an intervening green crop, or fallow; and enforcing these regulations by a specified increase of rent, in case of non–performance.   Adding, too, such alterations and amendments, as the progressive improvements of the country may from time to time suggest.

Proportions between Rent and Produce

In order an much as possible to preserve, that cordiality, which ought ever to subsist between a landlord and his tenants, there should undoubtedly be some admitted principle, on which their agreements are concluded. In this county, it is thought that the whole produce of the farm should he divided into three parts. Of these that one third should be appropriated for rent, another for the expence of management, and the remainder for the profit and subsistence of the tenant and his family. Great inequality must unavoidably arise from this proportion. For the tenant, occupying only 40 acres, will have but the means of bare subsistence; while, on the same calculation, the extensive renter of 500 or 1000 acres, with adequate stock and management, may acquire a fortune.

The example of Ireland, however, where powerful renters, or middlemen, prevail, does not encourage such a mode of cultivation. On the contrary, if instances may be adduced, where improvements have originated with great farmers, it will be still more easy to exhibit cases, where whole counties have been depopulated, by such a practice.

Perhaps the wisest system which human understanding can devise, after a complete division and appropriation of commons, and intermingled rights, will be to let every man rent or purchase, according to his means. Thus a distribution of property the most varied, from the petty tenant, and the smallest feuholder or copyholder, to the most extensive renter, and the richest lord, will take place; as is the fact in Ayrshire.

Character of Farmers

The farmers in this county, are a sagacious and observing race of men; and though wisely unwilling to adopt, on light surmises, every plan that projectors may suggest, yet, there are few instances of their long refusing to imitate such modes and practices as experience teaches, are adapted to the country where they reside.

Labourers

The labouring class of men in this county, who gain their livelihood by hedging, ditching, mowing, threshing, reaping, and other country work, are paid from 12d to 14d per day. They usually endeavour to have a small house and garden, which costs them 20, 30, or 40 shillings annually, besides a cow's grass, and sufficient ground for their potatoes.

Job–work—Rate of Articles and Labour

The habit of working by the job or piece is generally established, for every kind of labour. Hedges and ditches are made from 10d or 1s per fall of six yards. Grain is threshed from 10d to 1s per quarter; corn reaped and shocked for 5 or 6 shillings per acre; hay mowed for half–a–crown. Farm servants receive £5 wages for the half–year; and, if not fed in the family, are allowed 2 pecks of oatmeal and sixpence weekly for their maintainence. Women servants, for country work, £4 or £5 yearly.

Mason's work is generally done by contract with the builder. Journeymen masons receive 20d or 2s of daily wages, and carpenters are not less expensive. The price of building a rood of rubble work, two feet thick, and all materials furnished, from 25s to 30s. In consequence of the numerous stone quarries, bricks are little used in the county, and houses are seldom roofed with tile, which are neither so handsome as slate, nor so warm and comfortable as thatch.[o.f.]

> *Original footnote:* Little attention is bestowed on the art of making bricks. If the clay be not properly prepared, or if it be mixed with calcareous matter, they will certainly crumble and decay. The Romans made their

bricks extremely thin, and burned them till they vitrified. Many aqueducts and other public buildings built of such materials, remain at this day, in perfect preservation, in different parts of Italy.

Great quantities of oats and oatmeal are constantly sold to Paisley, Glasgow, and the manufacturing parts of Renfrewshire and Lanarkshire, and the quantities of grain and meal which have been imported into the county from Ireland, during the last ten years, are expressed in a note at the bottom of this page.*o.f.* The constant object of the landed interest, has been to raise and continue the price of grain above its natural level; at least, to prevent the competition of foreign rivals. For this purpose, applications have been made successfully to Parliament by this and other counties, to prevent the importation of grain, unless when the prices exceed the rates expressed in the last corn bill.[268]

Original footnote: Accompts of Grain and Oatmeal, imported into
Ayr, for 10 years preceding the 10th Oct. 1793, distinguishing each year.

Periods		Barley	Oats	Oatmeal	Pease	Wheat
From 10th Oct	To 10th Oct	Qrs.	Qrs.	Qrs.	Qrs.	Qrs.
1783	1784	20	40	..	10	256¼
1784	1785	..	628	990	..	..
1785	1786	..	..	..	..	..
1786	1787	1150	212	..	..	..
1787	1788	..	..	..	..	608
1788	1789	..	..	..	..	433
1789	1790	..	..	..	..	..
1790	1791	264¼	81	561	..	842
1791	1792	..	..	..	..	20¾
1792	1793	..	..	..	..	..
	Totals	1434¼	961	1551	10	2160

Custom–house, Nov., 1793.

Accompts of Grain and Oatmeal imported into Irvine and Saltcoats, for ten years preceding 10th Oct. 1793.

Periods		Oatmeal	Oats	Barley	Bear	Wheat
From 10th Oct	To 10th Oct	Qrs.	Qrs.	Qrs.	Qrs.	Qrs.
1783	1784	75	1361	..	..	..
1784	1785	1112	$5340^1/_8$	..	..	..
1785	1786	..	818	..	..	..
1786	1787	610	10691	2335	..	..
1787	1788	118	2222	..	..	$2374^3/_8$
1788	1789	..	..	..	..	$239^1/_8$
1789	1790	..	724	..	..	..
1790	1791	27	3838¼	637¼	..	..
1791	1792	..	2503½	..	..	..
1792	1793	..	..	..	..	..

N.B. –In 1792 48 quarters of wheat were imported; but it was afterwards exported. No other grain has been exported in the above period.

A great quantity of grain has been brought from Galloway of British growth, and some has been brought from Greenock, which was imported in that period.

Question concerning the circulation of Grain

Without entering into any disquisition, concerning the long agitated questions of limited or restrained circulation of grain, we may safely aver, that countries have uniformly prospered, in proportion to the security and facility with which the means of subsistence have been bought and sold. The removal of all restrictions of this nature, under Henry the IV, during the administration of Sully, first recovered France from the disasters of the league. On the other hand, the restraints imposed on the free sale of corn, under Colbert, tended as much to impoverish that kingdom, as all the extravagance of Louis the XIV.

Opening and Shutting of the Ports

With respect to Ayrshire, the continual juggling which takes place in striking the fiars, in order to determine whether the ports shall be open or shut, involves the country in a multitude of inconveniencies. Frequently, before the price of grain exceeds the rate at which the Legislature admits of importation, merchants foreseeing an approaching rise and scarcity of corn, would bring sufficient quantities of corn to satisfy the demand, but find themselves restrained by the apprehension, that when their vessels arrive, the ports may be shut, and their labour lost. Thus the prices rise, and the poor are distressed. Again, the ports by these means being opened, the merchants seize the opportunity, and dreading the quick shutting of the ports, bring such a sudden influx of foreign corn, as destroys the natural balance of the market, to the annoyance of the farmer. But when free export and import is allowed, these embarrassments do not occur. The exorbitant demands of the landholder and farmer are restrained by the foresight of the merchant, who, in his turn, is checked from overstocking the market, by the certain loss which would attend that measure.

Proposed establishment of Granaries

In addition to the unclogged importation of corn, nothing could be more conducive, to the accommodation of farmers, and interest of the labouring classes in this county, than the establishment of public granaries or magazines, in some central place upon the coast, where corn might be regularly bought and sold at the current prices. The profit to the undertakers, would consist in their being able to take advantage, of the fall or rise in the markets. The farmer would, at all times, be sure of converting his produce into cash when requisite, without the delay and trouble of milling his corn, and driving upon chance to fluctuating markets, while the public would be more regularly supplied, by the precision with which such an establishment would enable corn merchants and others to correct the scarcity in any particular district, by a quick supply adapted to the demand.

But a strong objection to such an undertaking arises from the prejudice entertained in this, and I believe in all other countries, against every species of dealers and traffickers in grain. In all times and countries, under the denomination of mealmongers, forestallers, monopolisers, and other similar terms, have they been the objects of public execration. There is probably no point of political economy more clear to philosophic and enlightened minds than the advantages which the public derive from that useful class of men. Their labours unavoidably tend to prevent the extravagant fluctuations in the price of grain, no less distressful to the tenantry than ruinous to the poor. Yet so deeply rooted in this prejudice among the lower classes in every community, that it would be unreasonable to suppose the Ayrshire populace exempt from an error, which at various times has occasioned dearth and famine in every age and country.

Operation of Manufactures

The operation which trade and manufactures have had on cultivation in this county is well deserving the attention of your board. The harbours of Ayr, Irvine, and Saltcoats,[o.f.1] were too defective, to admit of trade, sufficient to produce a direct influence on the character of Ayrshire husbandry; and there was no manufacture in the county, except of wretched articles for home consumption.[o.f.2] But the powerful energies of Glasgow, Paisley, Greenock, and Port–Glasgow operated an *anstouratio magna** in this respect.[o.f.3]

---

* A great [?]. ('anstouratio' not recognised.)

Original footnote 1: Those ports have only from 9 to 12 feet water at spring tides.

Original footnote 2: The shoe and carpet manufactures of Kilmarnock only excepted.

Original footnote 3: These towns, are in the counties, immediately adjacent to Ayrshire.

Glasgow

The opulence of Glasgow first arose from its trade in tobacco, sugar, and other goods, the produce of America and the West Indies. These gave rise to a great demand for articles manufactured in this country, with which the cargoes imported from the colonies were chiefly purchased. Thus the foreign trade of Glasgow called forth a multitude of manufactures, which overspread Renfrewshire and part of Ayrshire.

When the separation of America from England put an end to the great profits arising from the tobacco trade, of which about 50,000 hogheads, being one-half of the total quantity exported from Virginia and Maryland, had centered in Greenock and Port–Glasgow;[o.f.] the merchants withdrew from a concern no longer profitable, and the habits of manufacture formerly established in the country, enabled them to apply their capitals to the various branches of iron, glass, inkle, linen, woollen, gauze, and particularly of cotton, which, in a few years, they have extended to an extraordinary degree.[269]

Original footnote: These are the harbours of Glasgow, 18 or 20 miles distant from that city.

Paisley—Gauze Manufactory

About 40 years ago the town of Paisley was a small weaving place, containing about 4000 inhabitants, chiefly employed in working goods for the Glasgow merchants and the American market. A gentleman of great merit and ingenuity in that place, desirous of introducing the manufacture of gauze from Spitalfields, commissioned a few pounds of silk thread, proper for the purpose, from London.[270] After various counteractions, to which all new trials or inventions are exposed, he completely established the silk gauze manufactory in that town, where it has flourished with so much success, that there are now about 25,000 people in the place.[271] In a similar manner, the manufacture of checks and osnaburghs was introduced into Glasgow, about the beginning of this century, by a weaver who had served in Flanders and Germany, as a private soldier, during King William's wars, and on his return brought home the mode of working those valuable cloths, which he practised with great success, till they became a staple article of Glasgow manufacture.[o.f. 272]

Original footnote: See Ure's History of Kilbride.

Originally the patterns and designs of all fancy works, modes, and fashions, were composed at Paris, and issued out with an absolute authority all over Europe. But the Paisley manufacturers established draughtsmen of their own, by whom their designs were composed, and the patterns, when executed, were sent to London and Paris for approbation. By these means the inventive principle of modes and fashions, at least in respect of gauze, was transferred from Paris to Paisley.

The increasing demand for these articles induced the merchants to extend their business; and silk looms were employed in every village on the northern and eastern parts of Ayrshire.

Linen Manufactory

The linen manufactory had always existed so far in this county, that every family raised flax sufficient for their own consumption; and the women were all habituated to spin flax upon a small wheel, and to bleach and prepare the yarn, so made, for weaving.

The linen cloth thus manufactured, was in general of an inferior quality; and a spinner could hardly earn more, with great assiduity, than 4d a–day.[o.f.1] A number of small bleachfields were established throughout the country; but instead of rivalling the linen manufacture of Perthshire, or in the north of Ireland, it was visibly on the decline in every part of Ayrshire.[o.f.2]

Original footnote 1: Supposing her to win 12 cuts, or 1 hasp, per day.

Original footnote 2: Flax has in all ages been reckoned, as well as oats, a robbing crop. Virgil says: Urit enim, lini campum seges, urit avenæ. Vir. Geor. I, 77.[*] Columella confirms this assertion.

In Ayrshire, about 7 pecks of flaxseed are usually sown upon a Scotch acre, and, when the land is well pulverized, and duly weeded, produces, at an average, 20 stone of 24 lb English weight, worth about 12s per stone, 6d per pound, or £12 per acre. 2d per lb is paid for scutching; 1d for heckling or hatchelling; and when the flax spins into 48 cuts, per lb it will cost 16d for spinning. 1 cut, is equal to 5 score threads, or turns of the reel; 2 cuts make one hear; 12 cuts, one hank, hasp, or slip; 4 hanks, or 48 cuts, one spindle.[273]

---

[*] For a crop of flax parches the ground—this is true also of oats.

Flax worth 1s per lb usually spins from 36 to 48 cuts per pound. Tow, or hards, are sold as low as 5d; flax capable of spinning to 7 spindles per lb is worth 7s. Linen cloth for home consumption, worked in what is called a 1400 reed, costs about 7d per yard for weaving, and is worth 2s and 4d or half a crown per yard. Flax in this country, from some cause or other, seems to be by many degrees less vigorous and luxuriant, than that round Brussels, Cambray, and Valenciennes, from whence the fine lace, and cambrics are manufactured. It has however, generally been supposed that the Brussels and Valenciennes, laces were made from flax of the smallest stem and most slender texture.

Woollen Manufacture

The women, in all the labourers and farmers houses, were likewise in the habit of spinning, on very large wheels, the coarse country wool. They could not gain more by this kind of spinning than 4d per day, and the work is more severe than the spinning of flax; as, in order to twist the woollen thread, they run out the rolls of carded wool to a great distance from the wheel, pacing backwards and forwards 20 or 30 miles in the course of a day's work.[o.f.]

> *Original footnote:* Wool costs, for washing, teazing, carding, spinning, and grease, 2s and 6d per spindle. When worked into blankets, they are worth 1s per yard, and cost about 2½d for weaving.
>
> Home–made woollen cloth, 3 quarters wide, for labouring people, about 3s per yard when dressed. Such cloth dyed blue, costs for weaving, dying, dressing, about 10d per yard. The coarsest part of the wool is made into carpets, worth 3s per yard.

An attempt, on a small scale, has lately been successful at Maybole, in the centre of Carrick; to card, twist, and rove woollen yarn by machinery,[274] on principles similar to those applied in the cotton manufacture.[275] And no place can be better adapted for a business of this description. Indeed, the improvements in machinery of every kind, within these few years, and the application of the inventive faculties of men, in this county, have operated on every object, connected with manufacture and with agriculture.

Other manufactures have been attempted at Cumnock, and some other villages, convenient for procuring quantities of moorland wool. But Kilmarnock was the only place, where manufactures in the woollen branch were fully established; and there, the business being chiefly confined to carpets, little progress was made in the weaving of cloth.

Cotton Manufacture

By far the most rapid influence, however, on the condition of this country has been produced by the cotton manufactory. The manufacturers of Glasgow and Paisley entered very largely into this branch, as soon as the invention of Arkwright's machine was made public.[276] After engaging every eligible situation in their own vicinity, they directed their attentions towards Ayrshire. Cotton mills, on a great scale, were erected on the borders of the county, near Lochenoch, and Castle–Semple,[277] and at Cattrine[278] near Machlin, in the central part of Coil. Large houses, almost in every village, were filled with spinning–jennies, and moved by horses, where water could not be procured. The price of labour rose in every quarter, and the demand for cotton workers was so great, that farmers could hardly engage men or women servants, to remain at country work.[o.f. 279]

> Original footnote: A good worker, in one of these cotton houses, could earn from 2s to 3s daily; women from 1 to 2 shillings daily; and children from 1s 6d to 3s weekly.

The greater part of the cotton, worked in this manner, was furnished to the manufacturers, by the Glasgow merchants, who took them bound to return the thread at certain rates, according to its quality and fineness. This circumstance, renders it extremely difficult to estimate the annual amount of cotton thread prepared within the county. But, it is understood, that several thousand people were employed in this branch, notwithstanding the recency of its establishment.

Tambour, and other work

The operation of the manufacturing spirit, issuing from Glasgow, as its central point, diverged over this county, in every possible direction, and was by no means confined to the branches already mentioned. A number of workers in tambour and figured works on gauzes, silks, and muslins, established little factories at Ayr, Irvine, and in other places, where they employed several hundred girls and children.

Iron Manufacture

A great company from Glasgow established two blast furnaces at Muirkirk, on the estate of the Hon. Admiral Keith Stewart,[280] in the moorland parts of Ayrshire,[o.f.] with a view of making pig and bar iron on an extensive scale; and they already employ many hundred workmen, to the great advantage of that bleak uncultivated country.[281] Indeed, there are few parts of Great Britain so well adapted to the iron manufacture as Ayrshire; having abundance of coal, lime, and ironstone, in every district of the county. Possessing also the facility of importing, on reasonable terms, the rich ores of Cumberland or Lancashire, to work with Ayrshire materials, which are of a poorer quality.

Original footnote: The improvements carried on by this gentleman, do great honour to himself, and will be attended with much benefit to the country.

The natives are expert in constructing what are called snap dykes, 5 or 6 feet in height, with large stones bound and locked, in an ingenious manner. These, except in great storms of snow, enable the young plantations to be defended from the sheep. Thus shelter will be obtained. Drains, and lime, are fast changing the appearance of the pastures; and, with green crops, and sown grass in the bottoms, will enable a much larger stock, to be maintained.

The unskilfulness of iron masters, however, who remain still ignorant of the right mode of expelling from their coal, or cokes, the sulphureous particles, so prejudicial to iron, has occasioned many eligible situations to be rejected, on this account. The enormous expence and uncertainty attending the present system, on which this manufacture is conducted, together with the mysterious habits, and endeavours of those concerned, to preserve it in a few hands, has hitherto prevented it from becoming, as it ought, a source of opulence to this county.

Having been led for many years, occasionally to bestow attention, on the various chemical and practical operations, connected with the modes of smelting, and extracting iron from the stones and ore in which it is contained, and of reducing it into a malleable state, and into steel; it always occurred to me, that there was a radical defect in the whole system, which prevails in these kingdoms. Under this impression, I laboured, through a multiplicity of experiments, to discover the proper mode, of reducing the metallic parts contained in ironstone, and in iron–ore, into a malleable state, or bar iron, in one furnace, by a single process, without recurring to the bungling and expensive practice, of first smelting the metallic parts of iron–stone into pig, with all the subsequent and accumulated extravagance of bloomeries, chafferies, fineries, and air furnaces, before a bar of iron can be produced.

I have had the satisfaction to succeed in this endeavour, and have constructed a furnace which performs the purpose, mentioned, on such easy terms, and on so moderate a scale, as will enable any landholder, who has a few thousand tons of iron–stone on his estate, with an adequate supply of coal, to convert into a malleable form, without hazarding the expense of blast furnaces, and other extravagant establishments, seldom costing less than £20,000 or £30,000 before a shilling of profit is received. But, as this discovery does not refer, to matters of agriculture, I should not have alluded to it in this address, had it not appeared materially connected with the general improvement of the county, under our consideration.

Kelp—Fossil Alkali—Barilla

There is another article in which the county might derive advantage. The quantities of sea–weed, driven by every south and west wind, on its extensive shores, have been suffered to rot upon the sand, unless a few carts occasionally lifted for manure, and a still smaller proportion of the sea–weed growing upon rocks along the shore, which has been converted into kelp. The great demand for this article, arises from the fossil alkali which it contains, so useful for the purposes of glass; essentially requisite in the manufacture of hard soap, and also applicable to various processes in bleaching yarn.[of] As the fossil alkali is obtained from the different plants called wrack, sea–weed, or alga marina, and from no other plant, excepting the barilla, which grows on the shores of Spain and Sicily, its value has been constantly increasing, with the manufactures, in which it has been employed.[282] A ton of Barilla sells from £20 to £30; and a ton of common kelp from £4 to £5, and sometimes much higher.

> *Original footnote:* Fossil alkali, is the basis of sea salt, combined with muriatic acid, but no practical mode has yet been devised, for extracting the alkali on advantageous terms.
>
> The vegetable alkali, or potash, though very valuable, is by no means applicable to all the purposes in which the fossil alkali is employed.
>
> Above 2500 tons of fossil and vegetable alkali are said to be annually imported into Great Britain, and including kelp manufactured in Scotland, amounts to £7 or £800,000 per annum.

The mode of manufacturing kelp upon the shores of Ayrshire, and indeed on all the coast of Scotland, is barbarous in the extreme. An open kiln, or mass of stones, is placed upon the ground, about 14 feet long, 3 feet wide, and a foot or two in height. The sea–weed being previously cut and dried, is thrown into this kiln. The bottom is laid with sand and gravel, which impairs the kelp, and diminishes its value. The sea–weed, in the centre of the kiln, may be sufficiently heated to bring it into fusion, but that nearer the outside is chilled by the external air; and the whole, even in the best summer weather, is never brought properly into one equal mass of fusion. In this mode it is hardly practicable to make more than half a ton per day in one kiln. The weed, which, by the power of fire, has undergone the different processes, of evaporation and incineration, is brought at last into a melting state. It is then violently stirred with rakes and shovels; and when cooled remains a brown or blueish concrete substance, hard as a rock, pungent to the taste, and liable to attract moisture from the atmosphere. But imperfect as this operation is, it cannot take place at all, neither in rain, nor in wind, nor in frost. So that the process, requiring a long course of fine weather, for drying and burning of the wrack, can only be attempted during a few months, and, in bad seasons, only during a few weeks in summer.

In order to obviate these difficulties, I have contrived a kiln or furnace, which, with an apparatus sufficiently oeconomical and simple, dries, burns, and reduces into perfect fusion, the sea–weed in all weathers, and renders it a mass of kelp, pure and equal in its parts, and capable of being thrown in a mould or frame. Thus every sample is a true specimen of the whole, and contains no other refuse, than the earthy or heterogeneous parts belonging to the weed. These, by repeated experiments, amount to about 50 per cent, and the other half is taken up in solution, when the mass is pounded and mixed with a sufficient quantity of water. The refuse is mere insipid useless earth. The 50 per cent, taken up in solution by the water, contains all the saline and alkaline particles of every kind contained in the kelp. Of these, a great proportion are composed of common salt; others of sal–glauber; some of hepar sulphuris, while the remainder is pure alkaline salt.[283] These, by an expensive and elaborate process, may be perfectly distinguished, according to the priority in their form and system of chrystallisation, which enables them to be completely separated.

Experiments, which I have frequently repeated, prove, that Barilla contains nearly the same proportion of refuse, but the salts extracted from it by solution, possess a much greater proportion of alkali, as the common salt, Glauber salt, and hepar sulphuris, do not predominate in that preparation.[o.f.]

> *Original footnote:* The basis of common salt, is fossil alkali combined with muriatic acid. The basis is of sal–glauber, is fossil alkali combined with vitriolic acid. The hepar sulphuris is composed of alkali combined with sulphur; and sulphur consists of vitriolic acid and the inflammable principle, such as is produced by burning wood or charcoal.

As this process may be of material consequence to the great and ill conducted manufacture of kelp in the Highlands of Scotland, especially now, that the duty on coals carried coast ways has been taken off, I shall chearfully communicate the particulars of this plan, to any person recommended by your board.[o.f. 284]

> *Original footnote:* The abolition of duties on coals carried coastways, has conferred a greater benefit on those parts of Scotland which were interested in that measure, than any bill passed these many years. It is to be hoped, that the Right Hon. Mover, through whose exertions that bill was carried into effect, will add to his own fame, and to the advantage of his country, by moving the abolition, or commutation, of all duties and restrictions on the use of rock–salt, and on the manufacture of that useful article.

Opinions concerning Manufactures—Operation of them

The gentlemen in this, as in other parts of Scotland, under the influence of old feudal prejudices, had originally been extremely hostile to all manufacturing and mercantile transactions. But the enormous increase of rents, occasioned by manufactures, and the rise on all articles of subsistence, had conquered these hostilities; and of late years they had very generally afforded unqualified favour and protection, to the proposers of new establishments, in the way of manufacture.[285] Two material circumstances, however, have occurred to damp their zeal in these engagements.

In the first place, it is necessary to consider every country, and every branch of public operation, under the different gradations of an advancing, stationary, and declining state. During the former of these periods, the augmentation of manufactures, operates with most salutary impulse, on every branch of agricultural improvement, and of public prosperity. During the second, they may be considered as in a kind of neutral state; but in the last, or declining period, they become a serious burden and distress, on every order of the community. This is verified, by hard experience, in some provinces of England, where every proposal of a new manufacture is considered as a grievance and injury committed against the proprietory interest.

Disadvantages attending Manufactures

Although Ayrshire, and the Lowlands, on the west of Scotland, have for many years experienced a rapid and progressional improvement; yet every casual check to circulation, every accidental overstrain, or injury to credit, from whatever cause arising, has constantly subjected the country to the distressful scene of numberless manufacturers grumbling, unemployed, and destitute.

In the present instance, speculations in cotton, muslin, iron, glass, and other articles had been stretched to an extravagant degree. The quantity of spare money, and growing opulence of the country, occasioned an extreme facility of credit. The banks were led to grant cash accounts, or to discount bills almost without restriction. The consequences were, that every man engaged in profitable speculation, no sooner gained a sum than, instead of considering it as a capital, to yield an established income, he expended it, with as much more as he could borrow or procure, in extending his adventures, trusting always to the growing increase of advantage. Thus, a man who had gained £20,000 by twisting cotton yarn, with Arkwright's machinery, would build another mill of double power, and expend £20,000 besides the profit he had made. By these means, instead of becoming more easy and comfortable in his circumstances, every new success involved him in additional adventures and consequent embarassment.

While general prosperity pervaded every branch of business, the excess of enterprise, and daily failures which occurred, were only considered as indications of individual extravagance, or accidental misfortune. But the first public event, occasioning a pause among the speculators, which happened to be a declaration of hostilities on the part of France, acted like the injection of cold water into a beam engine; condensed the unsubstantial vapour, and the whole fabric came tumbling down.[286]

Conduct of the Banks—State of Credit

The chartered banks of Scotland, in imitation of the bank of England, finding that the minor operators had trenched on their advantages; and observing also, that the competition had involved them in a credulous, and hazardous excess of circulation; acting with a precipitancy, only equalled by their preceding relaxation, instantly recalled the credits they had so largely granted. Thus a country which, a few months before, enjoyed the heyday of prosperity, was suddenly cramped and palsied in every operation. Traders, manufacturers, miners, graziers, farmers, and landholders, all of whom had overstrained their speculations, found like Alnascar, that their basket full of brittle contents was broken.[287] The consequences were, that a clamour was attempted to be raised against the most just, necessary, and unavoidable war, in which this country ever was engaged; at a moment too, when the consequences of hostility could not possibly have materially affected any individual. Against this position, it is presumed that no one will contend, except those who would rather hazard, civil strife or invasion at home, than hostility abroad. Sober and reflecting men, however, recollect, that many of those speculators who have failed for several hundred thousand pounds, were never worth as many pence at any period of their existence. That the stoppage which occurred some years ago, in the cotton manufactory originated in the same causes, and as far as it extended, proved equally severe, although the country then enjoyed profound and general peace. Above all, that in the year 1772, the contagious distemper of overstrained adventure, similar to that which has come to a crisis in 1793, involved the country in general disaster, although the kingdom had not then been engaged in war for a period of 13 years.[288]

These facts undoubtedly expose the unsound principle, which has governed this country, respecting debts and circulation. The creditor is betrayed into pernicious confidence, by severe enactments against the person of the debtor, who in his turn, is allured by the ruinous facility with which credit is obtained, by habits of extravagance, or ill founded hopes of irregular advantage. In former times, the most rational improvement was checked by a total want of credit, even to the most responsible persons. At present, the country is periodically convulsed, by shocks, failures, and stagnations, arising from a defective and disordered system. Indeed, the acts in force, on the subject of debts and debtors, would tempt one to suppose, that a writ and a bumbailiff were considered as specifics for every evil which creditors, or the country at large can sustain from such transactions.[o.f.]

Original footnote: Some purse–proud persons talking of their wealth, were answered by a Glasgow merchant, who humorously boasted, that he owed more than all of them were worth. This seems to be the prevailing sentiment which governs the mercantile, manufacturing, and, I may add, the agricultural, proceedings of the country. The example of France might have taught us, that whenever the disbursements exceed the receipts, whether in a public or private capacity, the consequences must be ruinous. Perhaps it might be more for our permanent interests, rather to imitate the practice of Holland, where every man's exertions are proportioned to his means; and where no man can preserve his character, and be in debt.

Dangerous Principles among Manufacturers

But there is another point of view, in which the manufacturing part of the community are still more liable to imputation. It is by this class, that every doctrine of subversion has been cherished; and it is only from the same source that the established orders seem to dread any disturbance. When persons of this description, joined by others of distempered minds, insult society with permanent sittings, bulletins, secret committees, sections, municipalities, conventions, and tocsins, to which, had they proved successful, the Guillotine, in due season, would have been added, it is time for the sounder part of the community to form a phalanx round the Throne, in defence of the constitution. For it is to be hoped, that the subverters in this country will not, like the murderers in France, find a set of dastards, ready to shrink from their atrocities, or tamely submit to robbery and slaughter. In this country we may flatter ourselves, that if matters ever come to extremity, every good subject will be found, in the words of Shakespeare, "at least with harness on his back!"[289]

The result from this deduction is, that whatever benefits eventually may have accrued, to the cultivation of Ayrshire, from the stimulus of manufacture; still it is a dangerous instrument of improvement; while the plough and the spade have never threatened any peril to the country.

So far, however, from wishing to disjoin these interests, it ever has been my desire to see them moving hand in hand. At this very moment, in conjunction with other proprietors, being engaged in every possible exertion to establish a harbour at the Troon, on this coast, and a canal from thence to Kilmarnock.[290] And I trust, ere long, another shall take place from Irvine to Paisley, so as to give every advantage to the circulation of manufacture and produce in the county.[291]

Concluding Observations—Character of the People

It only remains for me to offer some concluding observations on the character and habits of the different classes, into which the inhabitants of Ayrshire are divided.

From the facts already stated, it must appear that they are neither deficient in activity, nor in enterprise, and that little more is wanting than to direct those valuable tendencies to proper purposes. The indolence of former times, and feudal prejudices among the upper orders, which formed lines of demarkation and repulsion between them, have fortunately been modulated into more active and easy habits. Improvements in dress, living, and conveniencies of life, have increased beyond all credibility. But the manners and morals of the different ranks, have by no means ameliorated, in the same proportion. On the contrary, the civil cordial manners of the former generation are wearing fast away, and in their place is substituting a regardless, brutal, and democratic harshness of demeanor. The former race, it is true, wasted their time in sauntering diversions, in smiths shops, and changehouses. But a strong spirit of religion, and deep impressions of morality, not unmingled with some portion of austerity, preserved the general character more free from crimes, and gross enormities, than the people of any country in Europe, perhaps, those of Switzerland alone excepted.

A variety of circumstances have concurred to efface these impressions. The trade of smuggling, which, to a great extent long prevailed on this coast, naturally introduced a looseness of practice and opinions.[292] Hence, arose the pernicious custom of drinking spirits, so generally prevailing, as almost entirely to have excluded the consumption of ale and beer. These evils were extended and confirmed by the distilleries, which though checked in their progress by recent regulations, are still destructive to the health and dispositions of the people.[293] Another source of immorality and perversion of principle, arises from the frauds and perjury, too frequently occasioned by the mode in which the business of the customs and excise is conducted.

To these, is added a great increase of dealings and transactions, in every line of life.[of] The levelling manners so prevalent among manufacturers; the frequenting of fairs and markets; the numberless jobbings, sales, and bargains, all tend to substitute a turn for speculation, in place of the sober, steady principles of order and economy, which Doctor Adam Smith, in his excellent treatise on Moral Sentiments, expressly states as constituting the essential ingredient, or rather the distinctive character of virtue, attaching to the lower classes of the people.[294] From whence that great authority avers, they never can deviate, without ruin to their families, becoming a disgrace and burden on the country, or falling a prey to the most dissolute and vicious courses.

> *Original footnote:* This increase of transactions, and its natural
> consequence litigation, is so great that 40 causes are often advised in a week
> before the Sheriff Court; and there are not less, than 700 or 800 causes tried
> in a year, before that tribunal.

Education

To correct these evils will require a better and more systematic plan of
education than hitherto has been adopted. The people of this country have ever
been distinguished for a laudable desire to procure instruction; insomuch, that the
poorest persons will frequently starve themselves to educate their children.

It is undoubtedly incumbent on the public to grant such means of education
to individuals, as may enable them to become useful members of society. It is the
immediate duty of the landholders in every parish to see, not only that the poor are
properly maintained, but that the children be instructed in principles of sound
religion and morality; that they be trained to industry, and afforded means of useful
information, adapted to their capacities and situation.*o.f* 295

> *Original footnote:* On this principle the inhabitants of the United
> American States have diffused a mass of knowledge through every district of
> their extensive territories, which is fast rendering them more skilful and
> enlightened than any other class of men.

Schoolmasters

Unfortunately in this country, as in other districts of the kingdom, the
provisions for the schoolmasters are by no means adequate. Men of capacity and
talents can hardly be expected to waste their lives, in the laborious task of teaching,
for a smaller sum than they could earn by handycraft. Besides a house and garden,
and the usual salary, at present, not more than £6 or £8 yearly, sometimes
augmented by the trifling perquisites of parochial offices, they ought to have an
addition of emolument, by an increase of salary.[296] No man should be nominated
but such as capable of making reports, surveys, estimates, keeping statistical
registers and records, and other operations, by which he might better his condition,
and be useful to individuals and the public. It is frequently remarked too, in this
part of the country, that they are extremely neglectful of the manners of the rising
generation, rather encouraging them in rough and boorish incivilities, than in those
acts of reciprocal kindness and urbanity, which afford the best, and most pleasing
characteristic of any people. A persevering attention, however, from the
landholders and clergy, with a proper selection of schoolmasters, and regular
examinations of the progress, made by the scholars, would check the growth of
these disorders.[297]

Clergy

To the clergy of this county, the public is already much indebted, and may derive still farther benefit from their exertions. The intelligence and understanding which distinguish the individuals of this deservedly respected order, together with their professional intercourse, among all classes of their parishioners, render them peculiarly adapted for the propagation of useful knowledge; not in matters of religion only, but touching temporal concerns, connected with the welfare of the community. The valuable Statistical reports, which you have received from the ministers of every parish in this county, with the exception only of one at present vacant, evinces their ability to promote improvement, and the attention they have bestowed on that interesting object.[298]

Landholders—Condition, Character, and Duties

With respect to the upper classes of proprietors, or freeholders, and commissioners of supply, there are about 180 persons of these descriptions,[o.f.1] (of whom 114 are voters) belonging to the county, with estates from £100 or £200 to £20,000 *per annum.*[o.f.2] [299] Several of these families have been of very ancient standing; but the greatest number of old families have, within the present century, been obliged to sell their property, embarrassed by the reigning spirit of conviviality, and speculation, disproportioned to their income.[o.f.300]

> *Original footnote 1:* There are also 5 or 6 Peers families, of great property.[301]

> *Original footnote 2:* The largest estates in the county are about £10,000 per annum; but the holders of them have property in other counties, which make their income £20,000 per annum.

> *Original footnote 3:* Many farmers have remained on the same lands for 300 or 400 years, and every right minded landlord gives of course the preference to old tenants. It is difficult, however, to obtain any considerable rise of rent, or to introduce a system of improvement, but by means of new ones.

Indeed, considering the expence, and inattention to affairs, connected with the situation of a country gentlemen, and natural tendency of counting upon imaginary rentals, long before they become real ones; including too, the prevailing course of entertaining, drinking, hunting, electioneering, show, equipage, and the concomitant attacks upon the purse, and misapplication of the time, it appears surprising that any property unentailed, should remain above two generations in the same succession; especially in this part of the island, where the gentry have not, as in England, the resource of clearing from time to time, their pecuniary embarrassments, by large sales of timber from their woods, hedge rows, and plantations.[302]

Without adopting any feudal predilection for birth and family, it surely seems desirable, that courses which have proved generally ruinous to the interest of proprietors, and in consequence have been attended with such serious checks to cultivation, and interruptions to prosperity, should be corrected.

The country has a right to look to this class of men, not only for stability of character, urbanity of manners, and that sentiment of honour and humanity, which constitutes the liberal features of a gentleman; but for the encouragement of all that is excellent in arts, embellishing or useful in the intercourse and transactions of human life. In the present state of things, men of high degree are only respected in proportion as they possess these qualities. When they happen to be marked by unpolished manners, or disgraceful conduct, they excite no other sentiments than those of indignation or contempt.

Unfortunately, the landed proprietors in this, as in all other quarters of the kingdom, were formerly accustomed to consider themselves, in respect of their estates, as merely *Fruges consumere nati;*[*] and in general were inclined to think, that they had nothing more to do than draw their rents and spend them, unmindful of the obligations imposed by the intimate relation which they hold with the prosperity and welfare of the country. But now a better spirit has gone forth among them; and undoubtedly, when such strong endeavours have been made, to decompose the principles and elements of which all civilised society is compounded, it requires the best exertions of every well intentioned individual, to prevent so mischievous a process from being carried into effect. Landholders, whatever their pursuits in life may be, are now generally conscious, that they owe their first duties and attentions to their tenants and estates. It is just matter of reproach for any man to be ignorant or careless in his trade, more particularly when the right performance of that trade involves the welfare of the most useful class of men, and the means of subsistence on which the whole community depends.

Examples of England, Ireland, and the Highlands

If it could be necessary to enforce so plain a truth, the landed interest of this county might receive abundant admonition from the examples of England, Ireland, and the Highlands of Scotland.

In the greatest part of England, all the ties of intimacy and attachment between the landlord and the renter are entirely broken, to the detriment of both. In Ireland, at least in many parts of it, owing to the evil system under which the land is let; neglect of education, and other circumstances, originating perhaps from inattention or misconduct in the landholders, the actual occupiers of the soil are

---

[*] Destined by nature to enjoy the fruits of the earth. (Horace, Epistles, Bk.1, 2, 27.)

poor and wretched, and impoverish the most fertile parts of the three kingdoms; often endangering the lives of any persons, who attempt to improve their country or themselves. In the Highlands of Scotland a system and order of society did prevail, which, although unfriendly to the arts of cultivation, called forth some of the best principles, and warmest attachments of the human heart; uniting, by mutual claims of permanent regards, the different classes, *under such strong connections, and nice dependencies,* as nothing but the avarice, extravagance, and inattention of the higher ranks could have dissolved.[303]

Perhaps the best blessings, which your Board can possibly bestow upon the country, will arise from restoring to their proper order, those necessary relations, which never can be inverted without detriment and danger. As the Diplomatic Body were rendered eminently useful in France,[o.f.] by collecting important political information in other states, for the use of that kingdom; so it is to be hoped that the British Government, by means of your Board, will procure for us a mass of knowledge, on the general subjects of improvement, unequalled, in any other age, or country.

> *Original footnote:* See particularly the valuable work called "Memoires concernant les impositions et Droits en Europe."

At all events, the public trusts to your establishment, for diffusing every useful fact, and ascertaining every solid principle that ought to regulate the management of land and its productions. At the same time, the energy with which your career has opened, affords well grounded expectation, that you will persevere, under the impression, so happily described by a classical author, who thought nothing done, while anything remained to be performed.

Nil actum reputans, si quid superesset agendum.[*]

FINIS.

---

[*] Regarding no task complete, if anything was still to be done.

Statistics of the Valuation and Contents of Ayrshire[304]

Ayrshire contains the Districts of Carrick, Coil, and Cuninghame. Its Extent if 90 Miles by 20 or 25: And its Contents are; Carrick, 201,603 Scotch acres, equal to 253,540 English acres; Coil, 192,440 Scotch, or 241,920 English acres; Cuninghame, 130,837 Scotch, or 164,480 English acres. Total acres in Ayrshire, 526,603 Scotch, or 662,065 English.

[In the following tabulation of rent, the sum following the parish name is the "Valued Rent Scotch", and the figure in brackets is the "Real Rent Sterling" – absent where Fullarton did not supply it.]

CARRICK contains 9 Parishes. Maybole, £9440 9s 7d; Straiton, £4387 1s 10d (£3000); Kirkmichael, £3289 4s 8d (about £3000); Girvan, £4480 2s 9d (£3200); Daily, £3265 10s 6d (£3300); Bar, 1493 5s; Colmonel, £6989 10s 5d (£3000); Kirkoswald, £4565 18s 3d (£4000); Ballantrae, £3551 10s 10d (£2000).

COIL contains 21 Parishes. Monkton, including Priestwick, £1856 10s (£2500); Craigie, including Barnwell, £3918 8s 1d (£4000); Riccarton, £3294 8s 8d (£4327); Auchinleck, £3462 15s 4d; Galston, £5630 13s 4d (£6000); Symonton, £2012 16s 6d (£3000); Coilton, £2930 16s 2d (£2000); Tarbolton, £6239 16s 4d; Muirkirk, £2257 0s 10d (£1400); Old Cumnock, £3784 (£3000); New Cumnock, £6026 (£3500); Ochiltree, including Stair, £7845 6s; Dalmellington, £1795 19 1d (£1700); Mauchline, £5410 (£3500); Sorne, £5232; Dundonald, including Corsbie Fullarton, £6344 10s 9d (£6500); Dalrymple, £1979 8s 2d; St Quivox, £2900 (£3500); Ayr, (£3700); Newton–on–Ayr, [no return].

CUNINGHAME contains 16 Parishes. Dreghorne, £3168 14s 10d; Kilmaurs, £7349 9 1d (£5000); Dunlop, £3613 14 6d (£3000); Loudoun, £5695 14s 4d; Kilbirnie, £2905; Stevenston, £1206 (£1200); Kilwinning, £6168 6s 4d (£6000); Stewarton, £8114 12s 10d (£7000); Kilmarnock, including Fenwick, £12929 4s 8d (£5400); Beith, £6115 14s 2d (about £5000); Irvine, £1988 12s; Kilbride, £3346 (£2530); Dalry, £6805 7s 5d (£6350); Ardrossan, including Saltcoats, £2840 16s 8d; Largs, £3801 10s 2d.

Carrick

MAYBOLE. Number of souls, 3750; population in 1755, 2058; length in miles, 12; breadth in miles, 7. Soil, various. Much light and improvable land.

STRAITON. Number of souls, 934; proprietors, 7; farmers, 33; cows, 2100; sheep, 20,000; population in 1755, 1123; collection for poor, £30; length, 15 miles; breadth, 5 miles. Chiefly pasture. Wild moors. Sow 600 quarters of grain. One farm of 6000 acres rented at £50.

KIRKMICHAEL. Number of souls, 956; proprietors, 6; paupers, 20; population in 1755, 710; collection for poor, £30; extent in Scotch acres, 10,000.

Chiefly pasture. About 1400 acres under tillage. Land lets from 3s to 10s per acre. Few horses, few sheep, chiefly cattle.

GIRVAN. Number of souls, 1725; proprietors, 10; farmers, 78; paupers, 36; cows, 1700; sheep, 5000; population in 1755, 1193; collection for poor £41; length, 9 miles; breadth, 6 miles. Two–thirds hilly pasture. Low parts arable. Along the shore abundance of coal and lime.

DAILY. Number of souls, 1607; proprietors, 8; horses, 150; cows, 1450; sheep, 5000; population in 1755, 839; length, 6 miles; breadth, near 6 miles; extent in Scotch acres, 17,000. Soil, various. Great part arable. Large tracts of moor. Plenty of coal, lime, and marle.

BAR. Number of souls, 750; farmers, 46; cows, 2000; sheep, 25,000; population in 1755, 858. Dry, hilly pasture. Some parts arable. Full of lime.

COLMONEL. Number of souls, 1100; proprietors, 17; farmers, 116; paupers 24; horses, 232; cows, 2900; sheep, 12,000; population in 1755, 1814, collection for poor, £20; length, 14 miles; breadth, 6 miles. Number of ploughs, 106. Hilly pasture; the bottoms arable.

KIRKOSWALD. Number of souls, 1335; proprietors, 8; farmers, 102; paupers, 21; horses, 300; population in 1755, 1168; length, 6 miles; extent in Scotch acres, 11,000. Fine land along the shore, capable of great improvement.

BALLANTRAE. Number of souls, 770; horses, 200; cows, 3000; sheep, 12,000; population in 1755, 1049; length, 10 miles. Ten miles square. About 12,000 arable acres. Only 800 are now in tillage. Extends 10 miles along the shore.

Coil [Kyle]

MONKTON, including Priestwick. Number of souls, 717; proprietors, 7, besides 36 freemen of Priestwick; farmers, 30; paupers, 12; horses, 92; cows, 220; sheep, 250; population in 1755, 1163; collection for poor, £22; length, 4 miles breadth, 2½ miles; extent in Scotch acres, 3500. Greatest part arable, excepting sand hills on the shore. Population in 1755, including Newton on Ayr, now separate.

CRAIGIE, including Barnwell. Number of souls, 700; proprietors, 16; paupers, 12; horses, 246; cows, 738; population in 1755, 551; collection for poor, £20; extent in Scotch acres, 5500. All arable. Full of coal and lime. Few sheep.

RICCARTON. Number of souls, 1300; proprietors, 8; paupers, 15; horses, 207; cows, 848; sheep, 69; population in 1755, 745; collection for poor, £24; length, 6 miles; breadth, 2 miles; extent in Scotch acres, 4736. All arable, except 138 acres. 60 ploughs, 131 carts. Coal and lime. Soil, deep clay. Farms from 60 to 150 acres.

AUCHINLECK. Number of souls, 775; proprietors, 13; farmers, 72; horses, 220; cows, 1000; sheep, 12,000; population in 1755, 887; length, 18 miles;

breadth, 2 miles. Great part arable. Clay soil. Large tracts of heath. Coal and lime.

GALSTON. Number of souls, 1577; proprietors, 50; farmers, 100; sheep, several thousands; population in 1755, 1013; collection for poor, £40; length, 13 miles; breadth, 5 miles. Above 7000 arable acres. Remainder high and moorish. No beggars. Occasional aid to old and sick persons. Two societies for relief of members unable to work. 30 acres of flax. 7 corn mills.

SYMONTON. Number of souls, 610; proprietors, 16; tenants, 25; paupers, 12; horses, 120; cows, 500; sheep, 200; population in 1755, 359; collection for poor, £27; length, 4 miles; breadth, 1¼ miles; extent in Scotch acres, 2900. All arable, clay soil. 2 mills. 2 alehouses. No felonies for many years. Cheese and butter annually sold for £1276.

COILTON. Number of souls, 667; proprietors, 9; farmers, 57; paupers, 10; horses, 115; cows, 750; sheep, 1240; population in 1755, 527; collection for poor, £50; length, 7 miles; breadth, 2 miles; extent in Scotch acres, 7080. Clay soil; tilly bottom.

TARBOLTON. Proprietors, 19; farmers, 130; horses, 386; cows, 1800; sheep, 500; population in 1755, 1365. Chiefly clay soil; greatest part arable; some heath.

MUIRKIRK. Number of souls, 1100; proprietors, 14; horses, 75; sheep, 14,000; population in 1755, 745; length, 11 miles; breadth, 5 miles. All moorish. Full of coal, lime and ironstone.

OLD CUMNOCK. Number of souls, 1632; proprietors, 6; paupers, 23; horses, 220; cows, 1000; sheep, 2000; population in 1755, 1336; length, 10 miles; breadth, 2 miles; extent in Scotch acres, 10,000. Cold soil. Coal and lime. 150 carts. Social dispensary for members unable to work.

NEW CUMNOCK. Number of souls, 1200; proprietors, 10; farmers, 80; paupers, few; horses, 400; cows, 1000; sheep, 20,000; population in 1755, 1497; collection for poor, £26; length, 12 miles; breadth, 8 miles; extent in Scotch acres, 50,000. High and moorish. Greatest part not arable.

OCHILTREE. Number of souls 1150; proprietors, 10; paupers, 20; population in 1755, 1210; collection for poor, £36; length, 6 miles; breadth, 5 miles. Mostly arable; only 4 grazing farms not arable.

STAIR. Number of souls, 518; proprietors, 6; farmers, 56; horses, 180; cows, 780; sheep, 300; population in 1755, 369; length, 6 miles; breadth, 2 miles. Soil, stiff clay; greatest part arable and enclosed. In the year 1736, when enclosing began, the people destroyed all the fences.

DALMELLINGTON. Number of souls, 681; proprietors, 4; paupers, 27; horses, 50; cows, 800; sheep, 8000; population in 1755, 739; length, 8 miles; breadth, 3 miles. Wild and moorish.

MAUCHLINE. Number of souls, 1800; farmers, 73; paupers, 30; horses, 240; cows, 1080; sheep, few; population in 1755, 1169; collection for poor, £50; length, 7 miles; breadth, 4 miles. Surface flat; soil, clay and arable. A Society for relief of those who cannot work.

SORNE. Population in 1755, 1494.

DUNDONALD (including Corsbie Fullarton). Number of souls, 1317; proprietors, 16; farmers, about 50; paupers, 7; horses, 355; cows, 1850; sheep, 1100; population in 1755, 983; collection for poor, £36; length, 9 miles; breadth, 7 miles; extent in Scotch acres, about 10,000. Soil various; much rich land; part hilly; on the shore sandy. 1600 English acres in rabbit warren. Coal, sea–weed; no lime.

DALRYMPLE. Number of souls, 380; proprietors, 5; farmers, 40; paupers, 7; population in 1755, 439; collection for poor, £11; length, 6 miles; breadth, 2 miles. Soil not deep; arable and improvable along the river Doon.

ST. QUIVOX. Number of souls, 1450; proprietors, 8; farmers, 30; paupers, 20; horses, 132; cows, 750; sheep, few; population in 1755, 499; extent in Scotch acres, 3500. All arable; 104 carts.

AYR. Number of souls, 4100; proprietors, 60; population in 1755, 2964; collection for poor, £150 (also contributed, £215); length, 4 miles; breadth, 2 miles; extent in Scotch acres, 5000. Land all arable; hospital for 60 persons; 10 schools, 250 scholars; 70 debtors; 73 criminals; 40 vagrants in 1790. A barred harbour.

NEWTON ON AYR. Number of souls, 1689; paupers, 18; collection for poor, £50; extent in Scotch acres, 350. Many vagrants; 20 ale houses.

Cuninghame

DREGHORNE. Number of souls, 830; proprietors, 20; population in 1755, 887; length, 9 miles; breadth, 3 miles. All arable. Average rent of land, 25s per acre.

KILMAURS. Number of souls, 1147; proprietors, 32; farmers, 53; horses, 150; cows, 1464; sheep, few; population in 1755, 1094; extent in Scotch acres, 4400. All rich arable land.

DUNLOP. Number of souls, 779; proprietors, 55; farmers, 68; horses, 117; cows, about 1000; sheep, few; population in 1775, 776; extent in Scotch acres, 5163. Fine pasture land. Sell cheese to the value of £4000 yearly. All arable, except, about 850 acres.

LOUDOUN. Number of souls, 2308; four–fifths the property of the Countess of Loudoun; farmers, 50; sheep, 1600; population in 1755, 1494; collection for poor, £50; length, 9 miles; breadth, 7 miles; extent in Scotch acres, 10,000. Three fourths arable, rest moss. 250 carts; 4 draw kilns; much coal. John Earl of Loudoun planted one million of trees.

KILBIRNIE. Number of souls, 700; population in 1775, 657. One third hill and moor, remainder good land.

STEVENSTON. Number of souls, 2425; proprietors 7; farmers, 20; paupers, 12; horses, 135; cows, 700; sheep, few; population in 1755, 1412; extent in Scotch acres, 3300. On the shore, the land sandy. A large rabbit warren. Fine coal.

KILWINNING. Number of souls, 2360; proprietors, 9, besides 60 feuers; farmers, 132; paupers, 36; population in 1755, 2541; collection for poor, £89; length, 9 miles; breadth, 8 miles. Rich land, all arable.

STEWARTON. Number of souls, 3000; proprietors, 128; population in 1755, 2819; collection for poor, £40; extent in Scotch acres, about 10,000. 90 ploughs. Of the proprietors, 120 are portioners or feuers.

KILMARNOCK. Number of souls, 6776; proprietors, 24; farmers, 80; paupers, 80; horses, 350; cows, 2000; sheep, a few hundreds; population in 1755, 4403; collection for poor, £100; extent in Scotch acres, 6000. Ale houses, 50. 3000 people manufacture goods worth £90,000 annually. Soil a strong clay, all arable.

FENWICK. Population in 1755, 1113. Partly clay, partly moor and moss.

BEITH. Number of souls, 2872; proprietors, 105; population in 1755, 2064; collection for poor, £45; length, 5 miles; breadth, 4 miles. All arable. Sell cheese to the amount of £4000 per annum. Coal and lime. About the year 1760, sold linen yarn worth £16,000 annually. 3 Charitable associations.

IRVINE. Number of souls, 4500; population in 1755, 4025; length, 5 miles; breadth, 2 miles. A small shallow harbour. Several charitable associations. The inhabitants industrious and affluent, without manufactures.

KILBRIDE. Number of souls, 1276; proprietors, 19; farmers, 40; paupers 7; horses, 155; cows, 620; sheep, 2000; population in 1755, 885; length, 6 miles; breadth, 3 miles. All hilly. Quantities of flax raised, usually sown after potatoes. 7000 yards of cloth annually sold, worth about 1s 3d per yard.[305]

DALRY. Number of souls, 2000; proprietors, 90, one of whom has one–third of parish[306]; horses, 300; cows, 1900; sheep, 1300; population in 1755, 1498; collection for poor, £60; extent in Scotch acres, about 12,000. About one third not arable, remainder good land, capable of great improvement. Coal and lime in every part of the parish.

ARDROSSAN (including Saltcoats). Number of souls, 1518; proprietors, 8; farmers, 31; paupers, 12; population in 1755, 1297; length 9 miles; breadth, 2 miles. Port of Saltcoats, small, but capable of great improvement. Great quantities of coals shipped for Ireland. Nine tenths arable, but chiefly in pasture.

LARGS. Number of souls, 1139; population in 1755, 1164; length, 9 miles; breadth, 2 miles. Little cultivated. Extends along the Clyde.

Valuation of the county certified by John Boswell, Esq., Clerk, £191,605 0s 7d Scotch. Real Rent, supposed to be between £150,000 and £160,000 Sterling annually. Population in 1755, 59,009 souls. [Population] in 1791, taking Sorne, Fenwick, and Tarbolton as in 1755, 73,892.

It is to be hoped that the Clergymen of the different Parishes will have the goodness to supply the means of correcting and completing the columns in the Table; the writer of them having addressed them respectively for the deficient information.

Note. A Map of Ayrshire is preparing by Mr Ainslie, and will be delivered when completed.

Appendix 1

Publications of Colonel William Fullarton of Fullarton

Fullarton, William, *Case of William Fullarton, Esquire, claiming the title and dignity of Lord Spynie*, London, 1785.

Fullarton of Fullarton M.P., William, *A view of the English interests in India; and an account of the military operations in the Southern parts of the peninsula 1782, 1783, and 1784*, London and Edinburgh, 1788.

Fullarton Col., of Fullarton, *General view of the agriculture of the county of Ayr, with observations on the means of its improvement; Drawn up for the consideration of the Board of Agriculture and Internal Improvement*, Edinburgh, 1793.

Fullarton, William, *A letter, addressed to the Rt. Hon. Lord Carrington, President of the Board of Agriculture*, London, 1801.

Fullarton, William, *A statement, letters, and documents, respecting the affairs of Trinidad, including a reply to Colonel Picton's address to the council of that island, submitted to the consideration of His Majesty's Most Honourable Privy Council*, London, 1804.

Fullarton, William, *A refutation of the pamphlet which Thomas Picton lately addressed to Lord Hobart*, London, 1805.

Fullarton, Col. William, *A letter to Field Marshall His Royal Highness, the Duke of York [concerning Thomas Picton (1758–1815)]*, Brentford, 1807.

Appendix 2

Weights, measures and money

Although English weights and measures were to be used in Scotland according to the Act of Settlement, in practice Scottish measures continued to be used throughout the eighteenth century. Standardisation was lacking, with some units varying according to locality or to whatever was being measured. This is a complex subject, which cannot be considered at length here.[307]

Weights

Similar tables will be found in *Ayrshire at the Time of Burns*. Here equivalent metric weights have been given. There is also Troy Weight, omitted here as having no relevance to this text.

Pounds occur in Wight's text only in connection with grass seed, whether trone, English or Dutch is not stated. Fullarton specified the English pound on a number of occasions; elsewhere the pound is not defined.

Trone or County Weight

Cheese, butter, meat, hay straw

		Metric equivalent
24 ounces avoirdupois	1 Trone pound	0.680 Kg
16 Trone pound	1 Trone stone	10.886 Kg

It follows that there are 24 avoirdupois pounds in a trone stone.

English or Avoirdupois Weight

Groceries and merchant goods

		Metric equivalent
	1 ounce	28.35 gm
16 ounces	1 pound	0.4536 Kg
14 pounds	1 stone	6.35 Kg
8 stones	1 hundredweight	50.8 Kg

Dutch Weight

Meal

		Metric equivalent
17½ ounces avoirdupois	1 Dutch pound	496.1 gm
16 Dutch pound	1 Dutch stone	7.938 Kg

Measures

By an Act of the Scots Parliament of 1685, the Scotch measures for the inch, foot, yard and mile were to conform to the English standard. However use of the fall, the Scotch mile and the Scotch acre was prevalent in Scotland until the nineteenth century.

Length

Scotch	Scotch	English equivalent	Metric equivalent
	1 inch	1.0054 inch	25.54 mm
12 inches	1 foot	1.0054 foot	0.3064 m
3 feet	1 yard	1.0054 yard	0.9193 m
37 inches	1 ell	1.0333 yard	0.9449 m
6 ells	1 fall	1.127 perch rod or pole	5.669 m
4 falls	1 chain	1.127 chain	22.68 m
10 chains	1 furlong	1.127 furlong	226.8 m
8 furlongs	1 mile	1.127 miles	1.814 km

In 1794 at a meeting of an Ayrshire road committee, the fall was stated to be 18 foot $7^2/_{10}$ inches "Imperial measure", equivalent in old Scotch measures to 18 feet 6 inches. At the same time the fall according to "the understood measure of Carrick" was 21 feet (presumably Scotch and so 21 feet 1.36 inches English).[308] This was material where a contractor had undertaken to make an English mile of road at so much a fall. By Imperial measure he was due payment for 284 falls, whereas by Carrick measure he would only be paid for 251.

Area

Scotch	Scotch	English equivalent	Metric equivalent
	1 sq. inch	1.011 sq. inch	6.521 sq. cm
144 sq. inches	1 sq. foot	1.011 sq. foot	939.2 sq. cm
9 sq. feet	1 sq. yard	1.011 sq. yard	0.8453 sq. m
1369 sq. inches	1 sq. ell	1.068 sq. yard	0.8929 sq. m
36 sq. ells	1 fall	38.45 sq. yards	32.14 sq. m
40 falls	1 rood	1538 sq. yards	1286 sq. m
4 roods	1 acre	6150 sq. yards (1.271 acre)	0.5143 ha

Volume

From Andrew Wight's note concerning measures (page 14), we can see that he was very precise about three units for bulk commodities such as grain: the Linlithgow or Lothian wheat firlot; the Linlithgow or Lothian barley firlot; and the Winchester bushel. He expressed their values in cubic inches to two decimal places. His figures may be used to express the Linlithgow measures in terms of Winchester bushels, as follows.[309]

	cubic inches	Winchester bushels
Linlithgow wheat firlot	2197.34	1.022
Linlithgow barley firlot	3205.54	1.491
Winchester bushel	2150.42	1

The following tables for wheat and barley measures according to Wight have been constructed using these conversion factors.

Wheat measures according to Wight (used for wheat, rye, peas, beans, salt).

Linlithgow	Linlithgow	Winchester equivalent	Metric equivalent
	1 peck	0.2554 bushel	9.004 litres
4 pecks	1 firlot	1.022 bushel	36.01 litres
4 firlots	1 boll	4.086 bushels	144.1 litres
16 bolls	1 chalder	65.41 bushels	2305 litres

Barley measures according to Wight (used for barley, oats, malt).

Linlithgow	Linlithgow	Winchester equivalent	Metric equivalent
	1 peck	0.3727 bushel	13.10 litres
4 pecks	1 firlot	1.491 bushel	52.53 litres
4 firlots	1 boll	5.96 bushels	210.1 litres
16 bolls	1 chalder	95.36 bushels	3362 litres

Note that a quarter is 8 bushels.

Lime boll

In Wight's account, the lime boll was five Winchester bushels, 169.4 litres (pages 35, 48 and 60). According to Fullarton it was just four, 135.5 litres (pages 82, 85, 87 and 106).

Scotch pint

Wight stated the wheat and barley firlots in terms of Scotch pints, from which the Scotch pint measured 103.4 cubic inches, equal to 3.078 English dry pints.

Scotch	Scotch	English dry equivalent	Metric equivalent
	1 pint	3.078 pints	1.694 litres
8 pints	1 gallon	3.078 gallon	13.56 litres

The pint only appears once in the two texts (page 37) and the gallon not at all.

Money

At the time of Union the English pound (Sterling) replaced the Scots pound as the currency of account and circulation, at the rate of 12 Scots pounds to one English pound. The Scots pound continued to be used for land valuations and in some other situations.

Scots

Scots	Scots	Sterling
	1 penny (d)	$^{1}/_{12}$ penny (d)
12d	1 shilling (s)	1d
13s 4d	1 merk	1s 1d
20s	1 pound (£)	1s 8d

Sterling

	1 penny (d)	
12d	1 shilling (s)	
20s	1 pound (£)	
£1 1s (21s)	1 guinea	

Both Scots pounds and pounds Sterling were divided into 240 pence. In 1971 the pound Sterling was decimalised, and divided into 100 *new pence* (now simply *pence*).

According to tables produced by the Bank of England, the pound in 1770 has an equivalent value today of £59.61; the figure is the same for 1780, and £54.02 for 1790.[310] This provides, at best, a very rough guide to present day values of prices and costs recorded by Wight and Fullarton.

Appendix 3

Lime

Lime was essential to the improvement of land in Ayrshire for agriculture. The heavy rainfall in the county leached calcium and magnesium from the soil, rendering it acidic and unproductive. The effect of adding either quicklime or slaked lime was to neutralise the acidity, and to make calcium, and magnesium which is also present in typical limestones, available for plant use. However, the eighteenth century improvers had only a rudimentary idea of the chemical processes involved in its production and use. Chemical elements were unknown. There was no periodic table. The idea that substances might break down into distinct, quantifiable parts was just emerging.

Joseph Black experimented with limestone and magnesia at Glasgow University. He found that they produced a gas when they were heated, which he called "fixed air"; we know this to be carbon dioxide. He determined the amount of calcareous matter in marle (a mixture of clay and limestone) by measuring the amount of gas released when it was heated. He determined that 40 parts of this gas by weight were equivalent to 100 parts of calcareous matter in the marle. This accords fairly closely to the molecular weight of carbon dioxide, 44, and the molecular weight of calcium carbonate, 100; 100 grams of calcium carbonate will yield 44 grams of carbon dioxide. Black's findings were published in his MD thesis, *Experiments Upon Magnesia Alba, Quicklime, and Some Other Alcaline Substances.* This was the first work on quantitative chemistry, and the first detailed examination of chemical action.

In modern terms the substances and processes are as follows:

Limestone is principally calcium carbonate $[CaCO_3]$.

Quicklime is calcium oxide $[CaO]$.

Slaked lime is calcium hydroxide $[Ca(OH)_2]$.

'Lime' may refer to either quicklime or slaked lime.

Calcium carbonate $[CaCO_3]$ heated in a kiln becomes calcium oxide $[CaO]$ with the release of carbon dioxide $[CO_2]$.

Calcium oxide $[CaO]$ combines with water $[H_2O]$ to produce calcium hydroxide $[Ca(OH)_2]$.

Calcium hydroxide $[Ca(OH)_2]$ combines with carbon dioxide $[CO_2]$ to produce calcium carbonate $[CaCO_3]$ and water $[H_2O]$.

Fullarton understood Black's work and refers to his lectures and experiments in his discourse; see pages 102 and 106. However some part of his ideas had percolated to the gentlemen farmers before then, as is seen from opinions and observations recorded by Wight. Note in particular the remarks on page 46: "Lime exposed to the weather many years recovers, by degrees, the air that was expelled out of it by burning, and in time returns to its original estate of limestone, and is consequently unfit for being a manure." That is to say, the slaked lime reacts with the calcium dioxide in the air to form calcium carbonate.

Limekilns

Quicklime was produced by adding limestone to a fire, which could be of timber but in Ayrshire at this time was invariably of coal, in a stone or brick kiln.[311] The coal and limestone were usually retained above a grating. The quicklime produced was a powder, which fell with the ash through to the space below. A kiln was charged with coal and limestone from above, and the product was recovered from below through holes at the base, which also served to admit the air required by the fire. This type of kiln was called a draw kiln. They were generally built into a hillside to provide access at the two levels.

It will be observed that the resultant quicklime was mixed with ash, but this did not impair its function in improving the soil.

SKETCH OF A DRAW KILN

CHARGED FROM TOP LEVEL WITH
LAYERS OF COAL AND LIMESTONE

HILLSIDE

KILN OF LOCAL STONE
POSSIBLY LINED WITH BRICK

GRATING
QUICKLIME AND ASH
REMOVED FROM BASE

Implements used at a limeworks in the late eighteenth century:[312]

> Iron tools £12 14s 7½d:
> including   18 Kiln bars and Pokers
>   19 Napping hammers
>   6 scrapers
>   26 spades and shovels
> Wooden tools £42 16s 5½d:
> including   24 earth Barrows
>   17 buckets

The economics of limestone burning (Cessnock)

The following figures relate to the Cessnock estate in 1787.[313]

1st.   The boll of lime by which we measure limeshells is the Winchester bushell and five bushells to the boll.

2nd.   A ton of limestone produces about nine bolls of lime.

3rd.   Coals allowed for burning the ton of limestone is two loads or $^1/_4$ a ton, as eight loads is nearly a ton at 112 to the 100 weight, as that is what both lime and coals is calculated and sold at English weight 16 pound to the stone.[314]

4th.   Both great and small coals is used in burning lime, $^2/_3$ great and $^1/_3$ small is the general custom. The difference of the expense is nearly the same altho the small coal is about one–seventh cheaper it takes a greater quantity.

5th.   The lime stone in this country is of different qualities. The general run is a fine blue stone which produces two bolls of flour, or slacked lime, to each boll of shells, some rather more.

6th.   The expense of coals for burning lime stone at the rate of

	£		
Two loads to the Ton as above at 6d a load	£0	1	0
Knapery and burning the tun of limestone	0	0	4
Raising the tun out of the quarry where the lair or tirring is of moderate depth viz. from 4 to 6 feet	0	0	10
Total expense of Knapery and burning a tun etc	£0	2	2

Appendix 4

Cost of enclosing and improving land (Cunninghamhead)

In 1782 Neil Snodgrass of Cunninghamhead, parish of Dreghorn, petitioned the road meeting at Stewarton for compensation. In adjusting the line of a road, a piece of his improved land had been taken; he had been given in return the land occupied by the old line. His loss amounted to the money he had expended on improving the land given up to the new road. The event was not in itself unusual. In this instance however, the calculation of compensation was recorded in detail and is reproduced below.

Stewarton [Tuesday] 18th June 1782[315]

[Present:] The Earl of Loudoun, John Dunlop of Dunlop, Sir Walter Montgomery Cuninghame of Corsehill, Major Alexander Dunlop of Aiket,[316] George Fullarton of Bartonholme, and Neil Snodgrass of Cuninghamhead.

From the minutes of which:

The said Neil Snodgrass also presented a petition Setting furth That his Dykes were thrown down and new Fences were made by him at his own Expences at Forming the High Roads through his Lands in Dreghorn parish, vizt. The Road from Irvine to Stewarton And the Road Leading from thence towards Kilmaurs. That he had also Suffered considerably by the Line of Road being Altered and thrown upon ground then lately limed.

Corsehill, Aiket and Bartonholme were deputed to "Examine the premisses and Report the Expences and Dammages." They gave in the following report.

The Committee appointed by a minute of the Trustees met at Stewartoun on the Eighteenth day of June Current; Major Dunlop preses.

And the said committee having viewed the ground and Dykes mentioned in the petition of Neil Snodgrass of Cunninghamhead given in to the Trustees, Did nominate and Appoint John Laught to measure the length of the Dykes, and limed Ground taken off for the new line, who having measured the same accordingly reports as follows:

That on the road leading from Irvine to Stewarton which was carryed through the Dykhead yard. The new Dykes thereby occasioned to be made, measure in length [42 $^3/_5$ falls].

That the following new Dykes were made on the road leading from Kilmaurs Occasioned by the alteration of that road viz.

	falls
On the West side of the road above mentioned	$32\,^1/_3$
On the East side	$15\,^1/_5$
On the South side	92
On the side of the old line of road between the Earl of Eglintoune's ground and Mr Snodgrass's	7
	$146\,^1/_2$

The limed ground now the said road from Kilmaurs including Dyke and Ditch and new headrig thereby occasioned to be made measures as follows vizt.

	Acre	Rood	Fall
The said road and South Dyke and Ditch One Acre One Rood and Thirty nine falls	1	1	39
The said headrig		1	24
Amounting to	1	3	23
That the Dyke on the north side of the old road which was taken down on the new road being made on a new foundation measures in length			$77\,^1/_5$
And that the foundation or path of the Old road which requires Lime, Dung, and other Manure to bring it near an equallity to the other ground Measures	1	0	24

Which report the said John Laught signs in testimony of the truth thereof.

And the Committee having considered the said report, and having also Inspected the Dykes, And found them to be six feet Ditches, The ordinary Expence whereof is one shilling per fall, besides the price of thorns which would be at the rate of 9 shillings sterling per thousand, and each fall would take Thirty three thorns.

And considering that four pence per fall is a usual allowance for taking down and removing an old Dyke.

And from their inquiry and best Information there was Above one hundred Bolls of lime laid on the foresaid ground now used by the new road which with Carriage etc would cost Three pounds nine shillings and six pence for each hundred bolls.

And having taken convincing proof that Mr Snodgrass is become bound to give lime at the rate of On hundred and fourty bolls per Acre, and Dung at the Rate of One hundred and Sixty Carts per acre to make the foundation of the old Road nearly equal to the ground now used for the new road. The Committee Appointed the said John Laught to make an Account of all the Expence of these Articles So as an Order may be granted for the payment thereof which Account is as follows vizt.

	£	sh	d
Account on the Road betwixt Irvine and Stewartoun Executed in the year Seventeen hundred and sixty nine			
42 $^1/_5$ Falls of Dyke at one shilling per fall	2	2	2
Thorns at Thirty three per fall		12	6
	2	14	8
On the Road from Kilmaurs till it Join the above road near Cunninghamhead			
146 $^1/_2$ falls of Dyke at One shilling per fall made in the year [1775]	7	6	6
4830 Thorns at nine shillings per Thousand	2	3	6
Lime 185 $^1/_2$ Bolls for the Road, Dyke, Ditch and Headrig at [£3 9s 6d a hundred]	6	11	7
Forming the headrig		16	0
For taking down 77 $^1/_5$ falls of old dyke at four pence per fall	1	5	8 $^3/_4$
	18	3	3 $^3/_4$
And for meliorating the foundation of the old road vizt.			
Lime for One Acre and Twenty four falls at the rate of one hundred and fourty Bolls per acre amounts to One hundred and sixty one Bolls	5	11	10
Dung at the rate of One hundred and sixty Carts per Acre which at Eighteen pence per cart being the first cost and carriage from the nearest place of sale	13	6	0
Lime & Dung Nineteen pound Seven shillings and ten pence	19	7	10
Amount of the foregoing Accompts			
Acct on the Stewartown road	2	14	8
On Kilmaurs road [£18 3s 3 $^3/_4$d + £19 7s 10d]	37	11	1 $^3/_4$
whole Amount	40	5	9 $^3/_4$

This "whole Amount" was due to Snodgrass with interest on £2 14s 8d since 1769, and on £18 3s 3 $^3/_4$ since 1775, and was all due to be paid out of the conversion money of the parish of Dreghorn.

The three trustees concluded their report with this observation:

> We are of Opinion that Mr Snodgrass should further have Fifty shillings as the Fee and Wages for a herd for his cattle for five months during which his grounds were laid Open by the alteration of the Road.

Endnotes

[1] Schama, Simon, A History of Britain: The British Wars 1603–1776, London, 2001, page 388.

[2] See page 74. All such directions refer to *Ayrshire in the Age of Improvement* unless otherwise stated.

[3] By the Annexing Act, several of the estates forfeited by the Vesting Act were annexed inalienably to the Crown; their rents and profits were to be used for "civilising and improving the Highlands of Scotland." 20 George 2 c.41 (1746), *Crown Lands— Forfeited Estates* (the Vesting Act); 25 George 2 c.41 (1751), *Crown Lands— Forfeited Estates* (the Annexing Act). See Smith, Annette M., "State Aid to Industry – An Eighteenth Century Example", in Devine, T. M., ed., *Lairds and Improvement in the Scotland of the Enlightenment*, Dundee, 1979, pages 47–58; also her *Jacobite Estates of the Forty–Five*, Edinburgh, 1982.

[4] Symon, J. A., *Scottish Farming Past and Present*, Edinburgh and London, 1959; see particularly ch. IX, "Improvers, the latter part of the eighteenth century" and ch. XIX, "Diffusion of Knowledge".

[5] See page 79.

[6] See page 17.

[7] See page 38.

[8] See page 59.

[9] See page 58.

[10] See page 15.

[11] *op. cit.*

[12] See page 142.

[13] See page 73.

[14] See page 73.

[15] See page 140.

[16] The letter is undated, but it was written about 1750. It is quoted in Robertson, William, *Ayrshire: Its History and Historic Families,* vol. II, Ayr, 1908, page 107.

[17] Wight, Andrew, *Present State of Husbandry in Scotland,* 4 vols., Edinburgh, 1778 (vols. I and II) and 1784 (vols. III and IV). There are six books: volume I, 1778; volume II, 1778; volume III Part I, 1784; volume III Part II, 1784; volume IV Part I, 1784; volume IV Part II, 1784.

[18] From volume II pages 495–6.

[19] From volume I.

[20] From volume I.

[21] From volume I.

[22] Pease: the pea plant; also the plural of pea.

[23] Bear, or bere, an old name for barley, specifically used for the four or six–rowed variety, which is hardier than the ordinary variety with two rows. The four–rowed variety is also known as big or bigg.

[24] Archibald Crawfuird acquired the estate of Ardmillan, parish of Girvan, in 1748. He was succeeded by his son, also Archibald, in 1784, but in 1793, while he was still a

minor, the estate was sold to his uncle, Major Archibald Clifford Blackwell Craufuird.

[25] In 1736 John Dalrymple, advocate, was adjudged heir, and took the name and arms of Hamilton of Bargany. He established the burgh of Girvan in 1785. He was succeeded in 1796 by his nephew, Sir Hew Dalrymple, Bt., who also took the name Hamilton. They are recorded variously as Dalrymple Hamilton and Hamilton Dalrymple. Bargany is in Dailly parish.

[26] See the illustration of a plough on page 94. "In ploughing three things are performed. A slice of earth is cut off from the general mass. This slice is removed some inches to one side. It is so turned, that it may expose a new surface to the air, and that what was formerly uppermost may now be buried. To the performance of these things, the construction of the plough must be adapted, and the work must be performed with as little labour to the cattle, and to the ploughman, as possible; and the ploughman must have it in his power to vary at pleasure the depth, wideth [sic] and position of the furrow. The first of these actions is performed by the coulter, the second and third by the sock and mouldboard jointly." (Small, James, *Treatise on Ploughs and Wheel Carriages,* Edinburgh, 1784, pages 11–12.)

[27] John Johnston in Loveston died 3rd January 1812, aged 81 (OPR 585/1, Dailly).

[28] Sir John Cathcart of Carleton and Killochan, 3rd baronet, succeeded about 1765. In 1783 he was in turn succeeded by his brother, Lt. Col. Sir Andrew Cathcart, who died in 1828. Carleton is in Sorn parish and Killochan in Dailly. The farm taken by Gavin Park was part of the Killochan estate.

[29] Thomas Thomson (1730–1799).

[30] Sir Adam Fergusson of Kilkerran, 3rd baronet, succeeded in 1759, died 1813. Kilkerran is in Dailly parish.

[31] George Culley (1735–1813), a Northumberland farmer. According to the *DNB,* he and his brother Matthew were famed in Britain, Europe and America; "Crowds used to visit his farms to see his experiments ... and his name was given to a celebrated breed of cattle."

[32] Robert Bakewell, born Dishley, Leicestershire, in 1725 and died there in 1795. He was a farmer whose farm was a model of scientific management and who revolutionized sheep and cattle breeding in England.

[33] The practice was to sow wheat in the autumn, producing growth through the winter. Where pasture was to follow the wheat in the rotation, the grass seed was sown in the spring within the cereal. The ground would then be in a drier condition for maximum germination of the small seed of the grass.

[34] Hummelt: dehorned.

[35] James Whitefoord of Dunduff came into possession of the estate of Cloncaird, parish of Kirkmichael, in 1726. It is Cloncaird that Wight refers to here. Dunduff (sometimes Dinduff) is in Maybole parish, on the coast. Cloncaird was purchased by Henry Ritchie of Busby after 1799.

[36] Sainfoin is a perennial herb, *Onobrychis sativa.* Lucerne, *Medicago sativa,* resembles clover. Both are grown for fodder.

[37] The river is the Girvan.

[38] John Ramsay was minister of Kirkmichael from 1766. He died in 1801.

[39] James Wright was minister of Maybole from 1770. He died in 1812. Hugh Pyper, bailie, Maybole, died before April 1784. There is a notice to his creditors in *Glasgow Mercury,* 29th April 1784.

[40] David Kennedy of Newark, parish of Maybole, on the hilly ground of Brown Carrick. With the death of his brother Thomas, Earl of Cassillis, on 30th November 1775, he succeeded as 10th Earl. The reference to him as "Captain Kennedy" is confusing.

[41] Dimmonts: dimment, a wedder of the second year, or from the first to the second shearing; also dinmont, a wedder from the first to the second shearing [*The Scots Dialect Dictionary,* compiled by Alexander Warrack, first published 1911; republished Edinburgh, 1988, with a foreword and introduction by Betty Kirkpatrick].

[42] Wedder (also wether, or weather): a ram; especially a castrated ram.

[43] Dunart: possibly Dunure. See also page 115.

[44] The farm of Tarfessock lies in the Galloway hills on the Ayrshire–Kirkcudbrightshire boundary (NGR NX360880). For Earl of Cassillis see endnote 40.

[45] John Stewart, 7th Earl of Galloway.

[46] The improvements were those of Thomas Kennedy, 9th Earl of Cassillis, who succeeded on 29th February 1760 and died on 30th November 1775. See also endnote 40.

[47] John Bulley "of the County of Essex, late tenant of Attiquin" died 2nd May 1803, and is buried in Maybole Old Kirkyard. His wife, Williamina Black, died at Doonbank 5th June 1810 and was buried in Ayr. (Mitchell, A. & A., eds., *pre–1855 Gravestone Inscriptions in Carrick, Ayrshire,* (Edinburgh), 1988, p.140.) His inventory is in the National Archives of Scotland, CC9/7/78, page 657.

[48] Surely Captain Kennedy had been 10th Earl for more than 2 years at the time of writing? See also endnote 40.

[49] The Home Farm (now the Visitor Centre) at Culzean, designed by Robert Adam, was indeed begun very soon after Bulley wrote to Wight.

[50] Middings: also midden.

[51] Quicks: white hawthorn plants set to form a hedge. Quickthorn is thorn used for hedging.

[52] Sir Adam Fergusson of Kilkerran; see page 17. Achandrain, also Auchindraine, is in Maybole parish.

[53] John Binning of Machrimore. Machrimore, also Mauchrimore, is in Maybole parish.

[54] Wellwood is in Muirkirk parish. John Campbell (1725–1789) was one of the subscribers to the banking company of Douglas, Heron & Co (known as the Ayr Bank). He was ruined when it crashed in 1772. See Brady, Frank, *So Fast to Ruin: The personal element in the collapse of Douglas, Heron and Company,* Ayr, 1976 (this appeared both in *Ayrshire Collections Vol. 11* and as a monograph); and Checkland, S.G., *Scottish Banking: A History, 1695–1973,* (Glasgow & London, 1975). His estate was sold, and in 1788 he was struck off the roll of freeholders. Note that Wellwood was purchased by Keith Stewart of Glasserton (see page 130). Campbell had earlier been a partner in Alexander Oliphant & Co., the Ayr wine importing business with a heavy involvement in commercial–scale smuggling.

[55] Milcraig: also Millcraig or Milncraig, in Coylton parish. It was the property of Sir William Augustus Cunningham, 4th baronet of Milncraig and Livingston. He was the eldest son of Lieutenant–General Sir David Cunningham and his wife Mary, the only daughter of Alexander Montgomerie, 9th Earl of Eglinton. (Rogers, Charles,

Boswelliana, 1874, page 205.) He married "Miss Udney" in 1785. (*Glasgow Mercury,* 7th July 1785.)

[56] See Appendix 2: Lime, page 153.

[57] Blainslie is the name of a number of adjoining farms in the northern corner of Roxburghshire (NGR NT5443), north of Melrose, and about 2 miles south of Lauder (Berwickshire).

[58] John Hamilton of Sundrum (1739–1821) was for 36 years convener of the Ayrshire commissioners of supply, and a very active roads trustee. Sundrum is in Coylton parish.

[59] John Steele of Gadgirth. He inherited the estate in 1749 through his wife Mary, daughter of John Chalmer of Gadgirth. The house of Gadgirth was in the parish of Coylton. The estate extended into the neighbouring parish of Stair, where Steele was minister and author of its *Statistical Account.* In that submission he claimed that, as a significant proprietor in the parish, he contributed greatly to its improvement.

[60] See the illustration of a brake on page 94. "The brake is a large and weighty harrow, the purpose of which is to reduce a stubborn soil, where an ordinary harrow makes little impression. It consists of four square bulls, each side five inches, and six feet and a half in length. The teeth are seventeen inches long, bending forward like a coulter. Four of them are inserted into each bull, fixed above with a screw-nut, having twelve inches free below, with a heel close to the under part of the bull, to prevent it from being pushed back by the stones. The nut above makes it easy to be taken out for sharping. One of a lesser size will not fully answer the purpose: one of a larger size will require six oxen; in which case the work may be performed at less expence with the plough." (Home, *Gentleman Farmer,* page 13; see endnote 110.) Regarding "coulter", see also endnote 26.

[61] The wild service, *Pyrus torminalis,* is a small tree or bush; it bears bitter fruit. The wild, or common, cornel is the dogwood, *Cornel sanguinea.*

[62] The pinaster, *Pinus Pinaster,* is found in southern Europe, where it is used for stabilizing sand dunes. Forests of pinaster are a valuable source of turpentine.

[63] "Acer majus", now properly *Acer pseudoplatanus,* is the sycamore.

[64] The rowan, or mountain ash, is *Sorbus aucuparia.*

[65] The bark of oak and birch was a source of tannin, used in the making of leather from hides.

[66] The bird cherry is *Prunus padus.*

[67] The larix is the European larch, *Larix decidua.*

[68] Platanus: a plane tree. The Virginian or occidental plane is *Platanus occidentalis;* the oriental platanus is *Platanus orientalis.* The London plane, a feature of city streets and parks not known anywhere in the wild state, is *Platanus acerifolia.* Steele was distinguishing the plane, which in Scotland and the north of England was commonly called 'sycamore', from the true sycamore.

[69] Polish oats: by which was meant durum wheat (*Triticum durum*), or durum; hard wheat with a high gluten content. Pasta is made from durum flour, which is also known as semolina.

[70] Richard Oswald of Auchincruive, born in Caithness about 1705, purchased the Ayrshire estate of Auchincruive in 1764, and died there in November 1784. Among many innovations there, he grew sugar plants in his hothouse, the first in Scotland, and

sent seedlings to his plantation in Florida. See: Hancock, David, *Citizens of the World: London Merchants and the Integration of the British Atlantic Community, 1735–1785*, Cambridge, 1995.

[71] Plashed: the shoots had been bent and interweaved so as to form a hedge.

[72] Barskimming was in the parish of Stair.

[73] The Lord Justice Clerk was Thomas Miller of Barskimming, Lord Barskimming. When appointed Lord President of the Court of Session in 1788, he took the title Lord Glenlee, from his Kirkcudbrightshire estate. He was created a baronet in 1788 and died in 1789.

[74] Lockerhill: probably Lockhartshill, to the west of Barskimming, where the river Ayr twists through a thickly–wooded gorge (NGR NS472252).

[75] See Appendix 3: Lime, page 153.

[76] Henry Hann, overseer to Sir Thomas Miller. In 1772 he took a tack of Mains of Barskimming. His farming practice is described further on page 51. A damaged stone in Stair Kirkyard records Sarah Swan, spouse of Henry —— in Mains of Barskimming, who died 3rd February 1769, and also Agnes Knox, spouse of Henry Hann in Bilboa [a farm between Barskimming and Mauchline], who died 3rd June 1803 (anon, *pre–1918 Gravestone Inscriptions from Cumnock & Doon Valley District*, vol. III, (Cumnock, c.1980), Stair 93).

[77] In most contemporary records the spelling is McClure. Shawood, or Shawwood, is in Tarbolton parish. Like his associate John Campbell of Wellwood (page 26), he was ruined by the collapse of the Ayr Bank. His estate was sold by 1788. He was involved in a lawsuit with his tenant at Lochlea, William Burnes, father of Robert Burns.

[78] John Campbell of Wellwood; see page 26. Adamhill is in Craigie parish.

[79] Lazy–bed: a method of planting on untilled ground, in which the seed potatoes are covered with manure and sods from adjacent trenches.

[80] John Campbell of Newfield. The estate of Newfield was in the parish of Dundonald.

[81] Ley: also lea; ground left untilled, or once tilled but now in pasture.

[82] Poaching: reduction to a muddy swamp by trampling.

[83] See endnote 31.

[84] Shamble(s): a slaughterhouse.

[85] Holms is in Dundonald parish. Nunraw is in East Lothian. James Dalrymple also had the Ayrshire estate of Craig in Kilmaurs parish. On 15th May 1780, Matthew Hay was executed for the murder of William Wilson and his wife at the nearby farm of Plewlands; their daughter, who was pregnant by him, survived. He had laced a pot of sowens with arsenic.

[86] Major Alexander Dunlop of Collellan, in Dundonald parish. He died in 1793.

[87] See endnote 32.

[88] Patrick Clark of Holmes, in Galston parish. He was a merchant, and died in 1796. He bought the estate in 1770 from Lord Marchmont. After his death it was sold to Mungo Fairlie.

[89] Sir George Colebrook. The estate was known as Grogar Mains, or Grougar Mains.

[90] Dr William Fullarton, surgeon, died 1805. He was first cousin of William Fullarton of Fullarton. See also page 61. Rosemount is in Symington parish.

[91] Hillas is in error for Hillhouse, Galston parish. Milrig, or Milnrig, too was in Galston. Bruce Campbell (c.1734–1813) also possessed the Galston estates of Mayfield and Sornbeg. He was factor for Grougar (see page 41) and Cessnock (see page 46). In 1787 Bruce Campbell was appointed collector for the county by the Ayrshire commissioners of supply. He was also a close friend and adviser to James Boswell.

[92] For draining of the Sundrum moss, see page 27.

[93] Elwingfoot: presumably Elvanfoot, Lanarkshire.

[94] John Campbell, 4th Earl of Loudoun (1705–1782). He was succeeded by his cousin, James Mure Campbell of Rowallan, who shot himself in 1786. The 5th Earl was succeeded by his 6 year old daughter, Flora Mure Campbell. She later married the Marquis of Hastings. Loudoun Castle is in Loudoun parish (sometimes called Newmilns parish).

[95] Lorn is in Argyllshire.

[96] Tares: usually the cultivated vetch, *Vicia sativa,* grown for fodder.

[97] Orangefield: see page 62.

[98] The road to Glasgow from Loudoun passes through the parish of Fenwick before entering Renfrewshire.

[99] Cessnock is in Galston parish. Formerly the property of Hugh Hume Campbell, 3rd Earl of Marchmont, after a short period under another owner, it was acquired in 1776 by John Wallace, a Glasgow merchant and second son of Thomas Wallace of Cairnhill (Cairnhill is now Carnell). Wallace's factor was Bruce Campbell of Milnrig (see page 42). In 1787 the estate was purchased by trustees of Miss Henrietta Scott, later Duchess of Portland. Her factor was George Douglas. See Mair, James, *Cessnock: An Ayrshire estate in the age of improvement,* Ayr, 1996.

[100] Sir John Whiteford of Whitefoord (1734–1803). He inherited Ballochmyle, Mauchline parish, in 1766 from his uncle Allan Whiteford, and resided there. Like other Ayrshire landowners, he was impoverished by the failure of the Ayr Bank, and sold Ballochmyle to Claud Alexander in 1786. For the bank crash, see endnote 54.

[101] James Bruce. Apparently not the James Bruce, overseer at Auchinleck, who succeeded his father in that position in 1741.

[102] This report by Bruce was reprinted in part in Strawhorn, John, ed., *Ayrshire at the Time of Burns: Ayrshire Collections Vol. 8,* Ayr, 1959, pages 42–46.

[103] Big, or bigg, is the four–rowed variety of barley. See endnote 23.

[104] See the illustration of a plough on page 94. The old Scotch plough was "a strong heavy instrument, about thirteen feet from the handles to the extremity of the beam, and commonly above four feet from the back end of the head to the point of the sock." (Home, *Gentleman Farmer,* pages 3-4; see endnote 110.) It was cumbersome, difficult to draw through the ground and did not turn it over properly. The sock is at the front of the mouldboard; see also endnote 26.

[105] The Northumberland farmer is Henry Hann, already mentioned above. See page 36; also endnote 76.

[106] Caulmstone is limestone. Caulm, calm or cam, can also be pipe clay, but this consists of aluminium silicate, and is not a source of lime.

[107] Lord Justice Clerk: see page 34.

[108] Spret: also sprat or sprit; a coarse reedy rush or grass. Carex is the genus of sedges, of which there are around 2000 species.

[109] Stot: a young bullock, usually two years old or more.

[110] Home, Henry, Lord Kames (1696–1782), *The gentleman farmer: Being an attempt to improve agriculture, by subjecting it to the test of rational principles,* Edinburgh and London, 1776. Further editions appeared in 1779 and, posthumously, in 1788, 1798, 1802 and 1815.

[111] Wight has "Lorn Castle". The castle is in Sorn parish.

[112] The Dowager Countess of Loudoun, mother of John Campbell, 4th Earl of Loudoun, died in 1779 aged 99. The estate was purchased by William Tennant of Poole in 1782, and then in 1795 by James Somervell, a Glasgow merchant.

[113] James Connell was minister of Sorn from 1752 to 1789.

[114] Alexander Boswell of Auchinleck (1706–1782), who became a Lord of Session in 1754 and a Lord of Justiciary in 1755; he took the title Lord Auchinleck. His son James brought Dr Johnson to the estate in 1773. Auchinleck is in the parish of the same name.

[115] The late Earl was William Crichton–Dalrymple, 4th Earl of Dumfries, also 4th Earl of Stair from 1760, who died in 1768. He was succeeded in the Dumfries title by his nephew, Patrick Macdowall. Dumfries House was designed by the Adam brothers (John, Robert and James); building began in 1754 (Sanderson, Margaret H. B., *Robert Adam in Ayrshire; Ayrshire Monographs No.11,* Ayr, 1993). The estate is in Old Cumnock parish.

[116] Commissioners and Trustees for Improveing Fisherys and Manufactures in Scotland, established in 1727; this body was generally known as the Board of Trustees.

[117] Drongan is in Ochiltree parish.

[118] John Smith of Drongan, died about 1788, and his widow in 1789. He was succeeded by his son Mungo, born about 1737, died 1814.

[119] William Fullarton of Rosemount: see also page 42, and endnote 90.

[120] Mrs Fullarton was Annabella Craufurd, third daughter of Ronald Craufurd WS of Restalrig. She died in 1826.

[121] The repetition of ryegrass occurs in the original. From earlier examples, perhaps ribwort was intended.

[122] Poached with cattle: see endnote 82.

[123] The estate of Monkton, in Monkton parish, was acquired by James Macrae, formerly Governor of Madras, who renamed it Orangefield. He gave it to his daughter, who subsequently married Charles Dalrymple, sheriff clerk of Ayrshire. Dalrymple died in 1781.

[124] This "great plain" is now occupied by Prestwick Airport. The house became the terminal building during the Second World War, and was later demolished.

[125] William Fullarton acquired the estate about 1711 and built a mansion in 1745. Fullarton is in Dundonald parish.

[126] Colonel William Fullarton of Fullarton; author of *General View of the Agriculture of the County of Ayr,* 1793, which is reprinted in this book, beginning on page 72. See also the biographical essay by Rob Close, page 66.

[127] Irvine parish church, built 1772–1774. See Close, Rob, *Ayrshire & Arran: An Illustrated Architectural Guide,* Edinburgh, 1992, page 56.

[128] John Bowman (1701–1797) (Devine, T. M., *The Tobacco Lords,* 1990 paperback edition, page 178). Ashgrove, in Kilwinning parish, was formerly Ashinyards; its name was changed by Bowman. He was succeeded by his widowed daughter Anne Miller.

[129] The former proprietor was Archibald Stevenson, died 1791. He acquired Montgreenan in 1755 and sold it to Bowman in 1778. Montgreenan is in Kilwinning and Stewarton parishes.

[130] Major Hamilton Blair came into possession of the estate in 1732. He was succeeded in 1782 by his son William, Colonel of the Ayrshire Regiment of Fencible Cavalry, who died in 1841. Blair is in Dalry parish.

[131] John Fullarton succeeded his father, also John, as minister of Dalry in 1762. He died in 1802.

[132] The major sources for Fullarton's life are the entry in the *Dictionary of National Biography* [*DNB*] and James Paterson's account of the family of Fullarton of Fullarton in his *History of the County of Ayr,* volume II (1852) [Paterson]. The 'Introductory Note' with which William Robertson prefaced the reprint of Fullarton's *General View* in his *Historic Ayrshire* (1891) is based very largely upon Paterson's account.

[133] In a narrative rich with Fullartons, mostly Williams, it seems useful to retain for the subject of this note the appellation by which he was generally known to his contemporaries.

[134] Fullarton House was demolished in 1966. The adjoining Stables, built by Colonel Fullarton to designs by the Adam Brothers in the early 1790s, survive, having been converted into flats in 1974. See Davis, Michael, *Castles and Mansions of Ayrshire,* Ardrishaig, 1991, pages 261–263.

[135] Paterson, 19. See also Wight's comments on page 63.

[136] On 14th July 1774 James Boswell's party for dinner included "the Laird of Fullarton and his mother." Boswell comments: "the company went away gradually till I was left with Fullarton, who drank nothing at all hardly, and [two writers], who were both very social." [Wimsatt, William K. jun. & Pottle, Frederick A., eds., *Boswell for the Defence 1769 – 1774,* New Haven and London, 1960, page 237] Mrs Fullarton died on 11th March 1804, at Fairfield House, Monkton. [*Air Advertiser,* 15th March 1804, 4a]

[137] Initially these were Alexander Tait, writer, who lived on the estate, William Wallace of Cairnhill (Carnell), advocate in Edinburgh, and Alexander Boswell, Lord Auchinleck. Wallace died in November 1763. See Wilkins, Frances, *Strathclyde's Smuggling Story,* Kidderminster, 1992, page 57, and *Glasgow Journal,* 17th November 1763, 4c.

[138] Wilkins, *op cit,* page 55, quoting from records of the Customs and Excise office at Ayr.

[139] Wilkins, *op cit,* page 56. The Temple, from which Templehill, Troon, gets its name, was built by William Fullarton, and not, as is sometimes said, by Colonel Fullarton. It was obviously in existence by 1767. It apparently had an inscription, *Baccho laetitiae datori, amacis et otio sacrum* [Erected to Bacchus, the giver of happiness, for friends and for leisure].

[140] Quoted in Paterson, page 19.

[141] In London in May 1778 he was introduced by James Boswell to Samuel Johnson, with whom they discussed Brydone's qualities. [Weis, Charles McC., and Pottle,

Frederick A., eds., *Boswell in Extremes 1776 – 1778*, New Haven and London, 1971, pages 345–346.]

[142] Fullarton's links with the north of Scotland are interesting. Seaforth was a close friend, while his wife was a Mackay from Sutherland. In 1785 he had petitioned the government, claiming his right to the title of Lord Spynie.

[143] When the Mogul empire centred on Delhi "collapsed in the early 18th Century a Hindu dynasty emerged in Mysore, only to be soon overwhelmed by a Muslim military adventurer, Haidar Ali. For the remainder of the century he and his son, Tippoo Sahib (Tippoo Sultan), dominated southern India from Seringapatam. Tippoo felt it necessary to challenge the growing power of the English [*sic*] East India Company, but he lost his throne and his life in the attempt in 1799. Mysore then came under British rule as an Indian state in subsidiary alliance and, under its restored Hindu, dynasty, so remained until 1947 when it was absorbed into the new and independent Indian Union." [*Chambers's Encyclopædia*, 1970, s.v. 'Mysore'.]

[144] The copy of Fullarton's *A Statement, Letters and Documents respecting the Affairs of Trinidad* (1804) in the Carnegie Library, Ayr, includes many testimonials from others who served in India, and Notes by Fullarton on the progress of his command.

[145] Paterson, page 20.

[146] Paterson, page 20.

[147] National Archives of Scotland [NAS], Calendar of Scottish Patents and Specifications 1712 – 1812.

[148] Marianne Mackay was the eldest daughter of George, 5th Lord Reay, who had died in 1768. His grandfather, George, 3rd Lord Reay had been "an active member of the Society of Improvers in the Knowledge of Agriculture in Scotland," being at one time its President, and had written "various communications on his experiments with sown grasses, inclosure and water meadows." By the 1790s the Reay estate was seriously overburdened: in a letter written in 1799, Eric, 7th Lord Reay, echoed Fullarton's comments on maintaining estates: "It was I may say my misfortune to succeed to a very extensive Estate producing little, besides many Incumbrances, at the same time giving me a Rank which I would wish to maintain with becoming grandeur."   See Bangor–Jones, Malcolm, "From Clanship to Crofting: Landownership, Economy and the Church in the Province of Strathnaver", in Baldwin, John R., ed., *The Province of Strathnaver*, Edinburgh, 2000, pages 49–51.

[149] Quoted in Brady, Frank, *James Boswell: The Later Years 1769 – 1795*, London, 1984, page 471.

[150] This is probably Alexander Bruce (1752–1829), son of James Bruce (1719–1790), the overseer at Auchinleck. He worked at Auchinleck as a gardener from 1777 until 1785, when he took the tenancy of Highfield, St Quivox, on the Auchincruive estate. (Hankins, Nellie Pottle, and Strawhorn, John, eds., *The Correspondence of James Boswell with James Bruce and Andrew Gibb, Overseers of the Auchinleck Estate*, New Haven and Edinburgh, 1998, pages 232–233.)

[151] NAS, CS 271/42936, Colonel William Fullarton against Alexander Bruce, 1801. The quotation is from CS 271/42936/2, Answers for Colonel William Fullarton.

[152] Paterson, page 20.

[153] Though Brady has suggested that the passage on the cost of keeping up an estate and appearance also refers to James Boswell, and his attempts to balance his income

from Auchinleck against his outgoings. See Brady, Frank, *James Boswell: The Later Years 1769 – 1795*, London, 1984, page 538.

[154] Ayrshire Archives, ATD 1/2, Trust Right & Disposition by Colonel William Fullarton, 28th April 1803.

[155] Isleworth church was badly damaged by fire in 1943. It is believed that the monument to Fullarton was lost at this time. Colonel Fullarton is also commemorated at the family's burial plot in the kirkyard of Irvine Old Parish Church.

[156] There are some illogicalities in the Fullarton family tree which remain to be explained. William Fullarton and Marianne Mackay were married in Edinburgh on 18th June 1792. Stewart M Fullarton married Rosetta Fullarton in January 1796: the event is recorded in the parish records of both Dundonald and Irvine. In the Irvine records (OPR 595/3, Marriages, page 41) she is described as "Miss Rositta Fullarton daughter to Col Fullarton parish of Monkton." Possible answers are that she was a natural daughter, that Fullarton had been previously married, or that she was his sister, though this latter seems unlikely as Fullarton's father had died in 1759, and Mrs Stewart M Fullarton bore children. She died on 19th October 1814 at her house in Albany Street, Edinburgh (*Air Advertiser*, 20th October 1814, 4d). Barbara Fullarton, who married Alexander Manners WS in Edinburgh in May 1820, is also called a daughter of Colonel Fullarton: she died at Douglas, Isle of Man, on 22nd March 1861. [*Kilmarnock Weekly Post*, 30th March 1861, 5e] This footnote is largely based on the inscriptions at the family burial plot in Irvine, and from www.familysearch.com.

[157] Fullarton of Fullarton, Col., *General View of the Agriculture of the County of Ayr with Observations on the Means of its Improvement*, Edinburgh, 1793. This was one of the county agricultural surveys produced under the direction of the Board of Agriculture. For a list of the surveys and those undertaking them see *Glasgow Advertiser* 29th November–2nd December 1793, page 772.

[158] The Board of Agriculture was created by William Pitt (the Younger) in 1793. Sir John Sinclair of Ulbster (1754–1835) was its president and Arthur Young (1741–1820) its secretary. According to the entry for Young in *DNB*, "We soon find him complaining of the patronising and thwarting conduct of Sir John Sinclair, President of the Board, and of his inept and precipitate appointments of incompetent persons to write the reports of agriculture in several counties."

[159] See also Strawhorn, John, "The Background to Burns: Farming in 18th Century Ayrshire", in *Ayrshire Archaeological & Natural History Society Collections* [henceforth *Ayrshire Collections*] *Volume 3*, Ayr, 1955; and Lebon, G. H. G., "The Beginnings of the Agrarian and Industrial Revolutions in Ayrshire", in *Ayrshire at the Time of Burns (Ayrshire Collections Volume 5)*, Ayr, 1959.

[160] See also Ian D. Whyte, "Before the Improvers: Agriculture and Landscape Change in Lowland Scotland c. 1660 – c. 1750," in *Scottish Archives*, Vol. 1, Glasgow, 1995 31–42.

[161] The indented notes such as this are footnotes from William Fullarton's original publication.

[162] See also bear, endnote 23.

[163] Poach: see endnote 82.

[164] Candlemas: 2nd February; a Scottish quarter–day. Quarter–days were fixed by custom to mark off the four quarters of the year, and were the days on which tenancies and other contracts traditionally began and ended, and when payments were due.

[165] Coulter: the iron blade fixed in front of the share in a plough; mould–board: the board or plate which turns over the furrow. See also endnote 26.

[166] Martinmas: 11th November; a Scottish quarter–day.

[167] Grots (also groats): hulled grain; *c.f.* grits.

[168] Wadset: a mortgage of property, with a conditional right of redemption.

[169] See MacKenzie, Ross, *Ayr's Export Trade at the end of the 16th Century*, Ayr, 1988.

[170] Carolus Sigonius (1523–84) was active in the study of history and antiquities. Potgesserus has not been identified.

[171] Emphyteusis: a perpetual right in a piece of another's land.

[172] A grain index of inflation? Comparison of wages and prices across decades and centuries remains a difficult exercise. See page 152.

[173] Alexander Montgomerie, 10th Earl of Eglinton, was born in1723 and succeeded in 1729. In October 1769 he was murdered by Mungo Campbell, a poacher and exciseman. "[T]here was more sympathy for the exciseman than for the noble, who had made himself unpopular alike by the misimprovement of his life and the still more irritating improvement of his estates, his changes of old customs, his interference with old tenants" (Chambers, Robert, *Reekiana, or, Minor Antiquities of Edinburgh*, (Edinburgh, 1833), p.163, as quoted in Graham, H. G., *Social Life in Scotland in the Eighteenth Century*, London, 1909, page 208).

[174] Alexander Wight, tenant of Muirhouse farm on the Omiston estate; father of Andrew Wight.

[175] Milch cow (or milch–cow): a cow giving milk or kept for milking.

[176] The banking company John Macadam and Co. was founded in Ayr in 1763. Douglas, Heron and Company (the "Ayr Bank") took over John Macadam and Co. in 1771. For the failure of the Ayr Bank, see endnote 54.

[177] Pliny the Elder, full Latin name Gaius Plinius Secundus (23–79 AD); Roman savant and author of *Natural History*. This celebrated and encyclopaedic if unreliable work was an authoritative source on scientific matters up to the Middle Ages.

[178] Virgil: Publius Vergilius Maro (79–19 BC). Regarded by the Romans as their greatest poet, he is chiefly remembered for his epic poem, the *Aeneid*.

[179] Pabulum: nutriment.

[180] Alexander Fairlie of Fairlie (c.1722–1803); "By steadily pursuing a plan of agricultural improvements beneficial to the soil, and of course to the landlord and tenant, he is entitled to the merit of being among the best practical farmers Ayrshire has produced." (*Air Advertiser*, 22nd December 1803, 4b.) His eponymous estate, formerly called Dreghorn, lay in the parish of Dundonald. Fairlie was factor to the Earl of Eglinton. Note that the author, William Fullarton, had married into the Fairlie family.

[181] "The rotation for long known in Ayrshire as 'the Fairlie rotation', – from Mr Fairlie of Fairlie, near Dundonald, Commissioner then for Alexander, Lord Eglinton – was introduced about [1780]. Under it the tenants were bound to go *regularly* over their whole lands (*outfield* and *infield*) with tillage crops and grass alternately, and to sow a fixed quantity of seeds with the last corn crop. The three years under tillage might

be oat, beans or bere, intermixed in whatever way suited the tenant's interest and his land best – a crop of hay being taken from the seeds, and afterwards resting in grass from five to eight years, according to circumstances – so much slaked lime, or so many cubic yards of dung, being spread over the sward ere again lifting. Some time after, however, many began to see that three successive crops were too impoverishing and consequently restricted themselves to two years under tillage, one year's hay, and usually not more than five or six years in pasture. This system of rotation yet prevails widely on all the *heavier* lands throughout Kyle and Cunningham." (Sturrock, Archibald, "Report of the Agriculture in Ayrshire", in *Transactions of the Highland and Agricultural Society,* 1866–1867, pages 29–30.)

[182] Archibald Montgomerie (1726–1796) succeeded as 11th Earl of Eglinton in 1769, on the death of his brother (see endnote 173). Like Fullarton he had a career in the army.

[183] The statistics and observations contained in Fullarton's "column annexed" appear below under the heading "Statistics of the Valuation and Contents of Ayrshire." No map was included in the published work, but the following note was printed at the foot of the Statistical Table: "A Map of Ayrshire is preparing by Mr Ainslie, and will be delivered when completed."

[184] For the failure of the Ayr Bank, see endnote 54.

[185] The Glencairn lands of Kilmaurs were sold by William Cuninghame, 11th Earl of Glencairn, to Alexander Montgomerie, 9th Earl of Eglinton, about 1720. He was succeeded by his son, also William, who acquired Kilmarnock and three fifths of the parish of Ochiltree about 1752. Kilmarnock was later sold by his son James, 13th Earl, to Henrietta Scott. James was succeeded by his brother John, on whose death in 1796 the earldom of Glencairn became dormant.

[186] For a lengthier discussion of these arrangements see Pryde, George S., "The Burghs of Ayrshire," in *[Ayrshire] Collections,* 2nd series, vol. 4, [Ayr], 1958, pages 8–49.

[187] Cato, Marcus Porcius, (Cato the Censor, or Cato the Elder) (234–149 BC); Roman statesman, orator, and the first Latin prose writer of importance. His only surviving work is *De agri cultura (On Farming),* a treatise on agriculture written about 160 BC and the oldest remaining complete prose work in Latin. This is a practical guide to the cultivation of vines and olives and the husbandry of livestock, also of interest for its information on old customs and superstitions.

[188] One guinea = £1 1s 0d. See "Money", page 152.

[189] Red wheat: "A variety of the common wheat, of a reddish colour" (*OED*). According to *Chamber's Encyclopaedia* (1868), "Red wheats are therefore preferred for comparatively poor soils."

[190] The genus *Solanum* includes both the potato, *Solanum tuberosum,* and the Deadly Nightshade. Plants of the genus produce an alkaloid, solanine, which can be toxic. Potato tubers 'greened' by exposure to light contain quantities of solanine.

[191] Turgot, Anne–Robert–Jacques, Baron de L'Aulne (1727–1781); French economist; an administrator under Louis XV and the comptroller general of finance (1774–76) under Louis XVI.

[192] Polish oats: see endnote 69. Dutch oats: not listed in *OED.*

[193] Blainslie: see endnote 57.

[194] Guinea or Indian corn is maize. In many countries this is grown not specifically for the grain or cob, but as a 'green' crop for winter feed for cattle in the form of silage.

Indeed in the Americas it is commonly used to provide all year round feed for housed cattle. Colonel Fullarton wisely suggests caution by indicating the frost sensitive nature of maize plants. The green crop has been grown in Ayrshire for some years now with protection employed against May frosts. The resultant silage is high in energy and excellent as a winter–feed for dairy cattle.

[195] Shock: a number of sheaves of corn placed upright together for support while drying and ripening.

[196] About 1775 Andrew Meikle produced the first practical thresher, a machine which separates grain from straw (Slaven, Anthony, *The Development of the West of Scotland 1750–1960,* London, 1975, page 70). However according to Campbell it appeared in 1786 (Campbell, R. H., *Scotland since 1707,* Edinburgh, 1985 (2nd ed.), page 25.

[197] Goose–grass, *Galium aparine;* a plant from the genus *Galium,* which contains about 300 species of low perennial herbs found in damp woods and swamps and along stream banks and shores throughout the world. Plants of this genus are also known by the name of cleavers.

[198] Pierre Poivre (1719–1786); French missionary and colonial adventurer who championed French trade with Indochina.

[199] Lucius Junius Moderatus Columella, born 1st century AD, Gades, Spain; Roman soldier and farmer, who wrote extensively on agriculture. Two works, written in a non–technical style, survive: *De re rustica,* in 12 books, concerning farming and country life; and *De arboribus* ("On Trees"). *Of Husbandry* (1745) is an English translation of these two works.

[200] Rutilius Taurus Æmilianus Palladius (4th Century A.D.) was the author of a treatise on agriculture, *De Re Rustica,* in 15 books.

[201] James Fergusson of Pitfour, MP for Aberdeenshire, was one of the leading improvers in the north–east of Scotland, and spared little expense in the development of his estate, near Old Deer.

[202] See endnote 26.

[203] See endnote 110.

[204] Quickens: the underground stems of couch–grass and similar grasses.

[205] Nidus: a place or material in which spores or seeds develop.

[206] See the illustration of Small's plough on page 94. James Small: see endnote 26. "Of all the ploughs fitted for a cultivated soil free of stones, I boldly recommend a plough introduced into Scotland about twelve years ago, by James Small in Blackadder Mount, Berwickshire; which is now in great request; and with great reason, as it avoids all the defects of the Scotch plough. The shortness of its head and of its mouldboard lessen the friction greatly: from the point of the sock to the back part of the head it is only thirty inches; and the whole length, from the point of the beam to the end of the handles, between eight and nine feet. The sock and mouldboard make one line gently curving; and consequently gather no earth. Instead of a wrist, the under edge of the mouldboard is in one plain with the sole of the head; which makes a wide furrow, without leaving any part unstirred. It is termed the *chain-plough,* because it is drawn by an iron chain fixed to the back part of the beam immediately before the coulter." (Home, *Gentleman Farmer,* page 4; see endnote 110.) According to Campbell, "Small's plough was the most notable innovation in farm

implements in the eighteenth century," (Campbell, R. H., *Scotland since 1707*, Edinburgh, 1985 (2nd ed.), page 25).

[207] Anthony Slaven comments that parallel stone drains were used in Ayrshire, particularly in the parish of Sorn, and were found to be effective, but expensive. More economical tile drains were in use in Essex, Suffolk and Staffordshire by 1815. The Duke of Portland introduced them to Ayrshire in 1826, at a cost of £5–£7 an acre. See Slaven, Anthony, *The Development of the West of Scotland 1750–1960*, London, 1975, pages 72–73.

[208] William Blair of Blair, Colonel in the Ayrshire Regiment of Fencible Cavalry, M.P., &c, succeeded his father, Hamilton, in 1782 and died in 1841. He was Colonel Fullarton's cousin, his father and Fullarton's mother, Barbara Blair, being brother and sister. His estate was in the parish of Dalry.

[209] Here the quicks may have been intermixed with wild roses; hence 'hips'.

[210] Gaetano Filangiere played a part in the Neapolitan Enlightenment. His *Scienza della legislazione* (1780–85; *The Science of Legislation*) is one of the most important works of the European Enlightenment. In it he supported equal justice for all, state intervention in economic affairs, and broad educational reforms.

[211] Huntingdon willow is another name for the white willow, *Salix alba* (also Leicestershire willow).

[212] Furze: gorse.

[213] Until 1805 the Ayrshire Road Acts required that the statute labour, or its monetary conversion, be applied exclusively to the turnpike roads, in addition to the produce of the tolls. Colonel Fullarton was taken to task for his inaccuracy by the minister of Ochiltree, William Thomson, in his *Statistical Account* for the parish. For an account of the Ayrshire Roads Trustees in the period 1767 to 1805 see: McClure, David, *Tolls and Tacksmen: Eighteenth Century Roads in the County of John Loudon McAdam*, ([Ayr], 1994).

[214] Mr Bakewell: see endnote 32.

[215] The Appian and Flaminian Ways were two of the Roman roads which led to Rome. The Appian Way began in Brindisi and the Flaminian Way in Rimini.

[216] Maximilien de Béthune, duc de Sully (1560–1641); as minister of Henri IV he contributed to the rehabilitation of France after the Wars of Religion (1562–1598). He promoted agriculture, and the repair of roads and bridges, rather than the luxury industries favoured by the king. Jean–Baptiste Colbert (1619–1683), French statesman responsible for the economic reconstruction of France under Louis XIV.

[217] Lord Cathcart: Charles Schaw, 9th Earl of Cathcart (1721–1776). He succeeded his father in 1740. His seats were Sundrum and Auchincruive, both sold about 1750.

[218] William Forsyth (1737–1804), *A treatise on the culture and management of fruit trees*. Clearly this pamphlet had been published by 1793. Later versions of it, some with additional material by other authors, are in the National Library of Scotland.

[219] The Scotch fir is *Pinus sylvestrus*.

[220] Joseph Black (1728–1799), chemist and physicist; graduate of and professor at Glasgow University. His account of his studies was published in 1754 as *Experiments Upon Magnesia Alba, Quicklime, and Some Other Alcaline Substances*. This was the first work on quantitative chemistry, and the first detailed examination of chemical

action. His *Lectures on the elements of chemistry: delivered in the University of Edinburgh* was published from his manuscripts by John Robison in 1805.

[221] "Fixed air," discovered and so named by Joseph Black, is carbon dioxide.

[222] This mine was at Parys Mountain, just outside Amlwch, Anglesey. "The Anglesea copper mine is said to have produced in one year, £105,000," (*Glasgow Mercury*, 12th December 1787, 396a). See Rowlands, John, *Copper Mountain*, Llangefni, 1966.

[223] Dickson, Adam, 1721–1776, *The husbandry of the ancients, in 2 vols.*, (Edinburgh and London, 1788).

[224] Muriatic acid is hydrochloric acid; vitriolic acid is concentrated sulphuric acid.

[225] An alum is a hydrated double salt, usually comprising the sulphate of aluminium with the sulphate of another metal, such as calcium, potassium or magnesium.

[226] Magnesia is magnesium oxide. It was shown to be a different alkaline earth to lime (calcium oxide) by Joseph Black in 1755.

[227] Gypsum is calcium sulphate dihydrate. It may be converted by heat to the hemihydrate, or monohydrate, known as plaster of Paris.

[228] Sal–Glauber (Glauber salt) is sodium sulphate.

[229] Fossil alkali is sodium hydroxide.

[230] Mr Bakewell at Dishley: see endnote 32.

[231] Florence flask: a long–necked flask, designed to hold olive oil (Florence oil).

[232] Slacked (or slaked) lime is calcium hydroxide.

[233] Larne, Northern Ireland. Ships from Ayr, Irvine and Saltcoats carrying coal to Irish ports, returned with lime as ballast. See Graham, Eric J., *The Shipping Trade of Ayrshire 1689–1791*, [Ayr], 1991; note, for instance, page 30: "the Mayflower of Saltcoats ... invariably returned [from Dublin] with a cargo of limestone and sailed directly back to her home port".

[234] "[At Belfast t]here are 2 sugar houses, 1 salt pan and another building upon a new principle, that the same fire may [boyle] the salt and burn a kiln of lime at the same time. It is objected that the salt is not so good, because the lime requires a slow fire, whereas salt requires sometimes a quick fire, at other times none, or at most a lukewarm heat." (Dunbar, John G., ed., *Sir William Burrell's Northern tour, 1758*, East Linton, 1997, page 51; note that "boyle" is a conjectural reading by Dunbar.)

[235] See endnote 220.

[236] Richard Watson (1737–1816), Bishop of Llandaff; publications include "Chemical Essays" (1781–1787).

[237] Barilla: 1. A maritime plant *(Salsola Soda)* growing largely in Spain, Sicily, and the Canary islands. 2. An impure alkali produced by burning dried plants of this and allied species; used in making soda, soap, and glass. Also an impure alkali made from kelp. See Bailey, Jim, "Seaweed Processing in the West of Scotland", originally published in *Historic Argyll*, no. 2, 1997, and reprinted in *Ayrshire Notes*, no. 14, Spring 1998, pages 14–17.

[238] Richard Oswald of Auchincruive. See endnote 70.

[239] John of Fordun, died 1384? See: *John of Fordun's Chronicle of the Scottish Nation*, edited by William Forbes Skene (1809–1892); translated from the Latin text by Felix J.H. Skene.

[240] Robert Lindsay of Pitscottie (c.1500–c.1565). See: *The history of Scotland; from 1436 to 1565, By Robert Lindsay of Pitscottie. To which is added a continuation by another hand, till August 1604*, Glasgow, 1749.

[241] Aeneas Sylvius Piccolomini (Pope Pius II) (1405–1464). See: *Secret memoirs of a Renaissance Pope: the commentaries of Aeneas Sylvius Piccolomini, Pius II : an abridgement*, translated by Florence A. Gragg; edited with an introduction by Leona C. Gabel (London, 1988).

[242] Jean Froissart (c.1337–c.1410); his *Chronicles* provide a vivid history of the Hundred Years' War. He also covered the Anglo–Scottish wars. See Contamine, Phillippe, "Froissart and Scotland" in Simpson, Grant, ed., *Scotland and the Low Countries 1124–1994*, East Linton, 1996, pages 43–58.

[243] *Epistolae Jacobi Quarti, Jacobi Quinti, et Mariae, regum Scotorum: eorumq; tutorum & regni gubernatorum; ad imperatores, reges, pontifices, principes, civitates, & alios, ab anno 1505, ad annum 1545*, Edinburgh, 1722–1724. This consists of correspondence of James IV 1473–1513; James V 1512–1542; Mary, 1542–1587; and other information concerning 16th century Scottish history. The work contains material by the three monarchs, and also by Thomas Ruddiman, 1674–1757.

[244] Georges–Louis Leclerc Buffon (1707–1788), Comte de Buffon; French naturalist, author of a comprehensive work on natural history, *Histoire naturelle, générale et particulière*, which he began in 1749. He was created a count in 1773.

[245] Polled: naturally hornless.

[246] See Hugh Bone, "The Ayrshire Breed of Cattle", in *Ayrshire Collections Volume 1*, Ayr, 1950.

[247] Hugh Hume Campbell, third Earl of Marchmont, succeeded his father in 1740. He sold Cessnock about 1770 and died in Hemel Hempstead in 1794. John Boyle, third Earl of Glasgow, succeeded his father in 1740 and died at the family seat of Kelburn, Largs, in 1775. His son George Boyle, fourth Earl, was created Baron Ross of Hawkhead in 1815, and died in 1843.

[248] Bruce Campbell: see endnote 91.

[249] Two recent books on the history of dairying and cheesemaking in Scotland are: Gray, Adam, *White Gold? Scotland's Dairying in the Past*, Wigtown, 1995; and Smith, John, *Cheesemaking in Scotland: A History*, Clydebank, 1995.

[250] Thomas Kennedy of Dunure, who succeeded to the estate in 1765 and died in 1819. He owned the estate of Dalquharran in the valley of the Water of Girvan. See also the reference by Wight to the sheep at "Dunart ... on a range of hills on the sea coast", page 22.

[251] Weather: i.e. wether, a ram; especially a castrated ram. See also wedder, endnote 42.

[252] Moor–ill: cf. moor–evil, a kind of dysentery in sheep and cattle. Murrain: cattle plague. Grease: a disease which attacks the hooves of horses. Strangles: a infectious febrile disease of horses caused by the bacterium *Streptoccus equi*.

[253] British Wool Society: presumably the Society for the Improvement of British Wool, another of Sir John Sinclair's ventures. Among those present at a Sheep–Shearing Festival held by the Society in Edinburgh in 1791 was the "venerable patriotic Dowager Countess of Dundonald , whose hat was decorated with a bandeau of wool from her own flock, and dyed by herself of various beautiful vivid colours, which had a fine effect." (*Glasgow Mercury,* 8th July 1791, 437b). The Countess was

Jean Stuart (c.1722–1808), second wife of Thomas Cochrane, 8th Earl of Dundonald.

[254] Colchis: ancient region at the eastern end of the Black Sea, south of the Caucasus; now part of Georgia. Trebisonde: Trebizond on the Black Sea; now Trabzon, Turkey.

[255] Pontus: ancient district in north–eastern Anatolia adjoining the Black Sea. Angora: district in Asia Minor. Ancyra: modern Ankara, capital of Turkey.

[256] George Culley: see endnote 31.

[257] Juan Enrique de Graef, whose *Discursos Mercuriales* was published in 1755–1756. René–Antoine Ferchault de Réaumur (1683–1757); French scientist of the early 18th century.

[258] John Hunter (1728–1793); surgeon, founder of pathological anatomy in England. Championed the value of investigation and experimentation, contributing to the cause his own work in comparative biology, anatomy, physiology, and pathology.

[259] Sir Joseph Banks, baronet (1743–1820); British explorer and naturalist; he sailed with Captain Cook, and was for many years president of the Royal Society.

[260] Esculent: edible. The Morea: the Peloponnese (Greece).

[261] The current National Botanic Gardens at Cape Town – the Kirstenbosch Botanic Garden – were only established in 1913.

[262] A Botanical Garden was established in Lisbon in the mid 18th Century by Gerard de Visme, a British merchant (and Huguenot refugee), born in London in 1726. The present Jardim Botanico dates from 1874.

[263] Fort St. George: a fort built by the East India Company in Madras, India. According to the *DNB*, James Anderson (died 1809) was Physician–General of the company in Madras. He was in India from about 1765, and corresponded with botanists such as Joseph Banks (see endnote 259). His publications concerned his attempts to 'farm' cochineal, to introduce silk cultivation, the potential for production of sugar cane, cotton, &c., in India, and other subjects.

[264] Fatak, *Panicum maximum*, remains a widely–used cattle fodder crop in Mauritius.

[265] Ervum: a type of lentil or vetch, One species, *Ervum lens*, is known to the Indians as masur. Ocymum: probably *Ocimum basilicum*, or basil. Cytisus: broom.

[266] Lote tree: possibly *Lotus corniculatus*, the bird's–foot trefoil, often used as a forage for cattle. The *OED* gives two options: the nettle tree, *Celtis australis;* and the jujube tree, *Ziziphus lotus.*

[267] Smith, Adam (1723–1790), *An Inquiry into the Nature and Causes of the Wealth of Nations,* London, 1776. He thought, for instance, that "the law ought always to trust people with the care of their own interest, as in their local situations they must generally be able to judge better of it than the legislator can do." (Book IV, chap. V, from "Digression concerning the corn trade and corn laws".)

[268] The noblemen, gentlemen, freeholders and commissioners of supply of Ayrshire resolved to oppose Pitt's plan for a customs union with Ireland, in so far as it entailed relaxation of the duty imposed on Irish grain. The plan was also opposed by manufacturers; though the proximate cause of its failure was the refusal of the Irish Parliament to contribute to the cost of Imperial defence. Ayrshire Archives, CO3/1/3, minutes of the Ayrshire commissioners of supply, 13th October 1786.

[269] Inkle: a tape made of linen, or the thread or yarn from which it is made.

[270] See Clark, Sylvia, *Paisley: A History,* Edinburgh, 1988, page 26: "In 1759 a pair of Paisley corks named Fulton and McKerrel, both incomers from the thriving countryside to the west, set their weavers to making silk gauze like that made by the Spitalfields weavers in London." 'Cork' was a colloquial term for a manufacturer's agent, the vital link between the weavers and the yarn and cloth merchants.

[271] The population of Paisley was 6,799 in 1751; 17,026 in 1801.

[272] Osnaburg: coarse linen of a type made in Osnabrück, Germany.

[273] Scutching: dressing fibrous material, such as flax or hemp, by beating it. Notwithstanding the definition, 'scutching' implied more than beating, according to the following announcement. In 1792 the "possessors of Lint–mills" in a number of Ayrshire parishes announced these charges: "for beating lint eighteenpence per stone, tron weight", and "for skutching two shillings and eightpence per stone, tron weight" (*Glasgow Advertiser,* 15th October 1792). Hatchel (or heckle): a device for combing flax or hemp; hence hatchelling or heckling.

[274] Rove: to draw out and twist small pieces of a fibrous material such as cotton or wool.

[275] This is probably a reference to the woollen mill at Minishant, in Maybole parish, established in the late eighteenth century. Latterly a blanket and tweed mill, it was converted into a village hall in 1925. See Douglas, Henrietta and Hugh, *Minishant is a Bonnie Wee Place,* 1982.

[276] Richard Arkwright's patented water–powered frame (1769) produced a strong yarn which was suitable for warp. James Hargreave's spinning jenny (invented about 1767) produced a weaker thread suitable only for weft. The warp threads are those which run lengthwise in a loom, whereas the weft threads run from side to side.

[277] Lochenoch: Lochwinnoch, which is on Castle Semple Loch. The Lochwinnoch mill was in Renfrewshire, on the estate of Knockbartnock, about three miles from the Ayrshire boundary. When the "newly built" mill, the property of William Caldwell and Company, was offered for sale in 1794, it consisted of three stories, about 76 feet by 30 feet, with "an excellent water wheel, and other machinery ... capable for executing work to the best advantage both in preparation and spinning." Also included was a "factory" in the village of Lochwinnoch, with "eighteen mule Jennies, two Stretching Frames, and other machinery" (*Glasgow Advertiser* 7th February 1794, 88).

[278] Catrine, in the parish of Sorn: Claud Alexander purchased the estate of Ballochmyle in 1786 and established a cotton mill there with the assistance of David Dale; by 1793 there was a community of 1350, with extensive works, a school and a church. Rev. George Gordon wrote in 1797 in the *Statistical Account*: "beside highly improving his landed property, he has built the cotton–mills and village of Catrine, which have infused life and activity into this part of the country."

[279] Labour was drawn to the new industries from neighbouring parishes. Kirkconnel, Dumfriesshire, 17 miles from Catrine, was one of the areas affected. The parish minister, John Robertson lamented the impact of manufactures on the availability of farm servants in an extended footnote in his *Statistical Account* contribution, from which the following is taken: "Agriculture must fall into decay . . . what else is to be expected, when the very money, paid by the farmer and others, for statute labour and at toll–bars, is employed against him to augment his hardships, by being lavishly held out in tempting offers to his servants and labourers, to entice them from his

work, and induce them to go to the making and repairing of the great roads;
especially, when the mineries, founderies, and the like great works, above all the
cotton manufactures, all around, particularly in the west, have swept the country
quite bare of hands, and seem as if they could still keep it in the same situation?"

[280] Keith Stewart, Receiver General of the Land Tax in Scotland and brother of John, 7th
Earl of Galloway, acquired land in Muirkirk parish in the 1780s. According to a
game preservation advertisement in 1789, he owned "the Wellwoods [Upper and
Middle], Kaims and Kaimshill" and other unspecified lands (*Glasgow Mercury,* 14th
July 1789, 231). His seat was at Glasserton, Wigtownshire.

[281] See Hume, John R., and Butt, J., "The creation of a Scottish industrial community," in
Scottish Historical Review Volume 45, 1960, pages 160–183; and Campbell, R. H.,
"The Iron Industry in Ayrshire", in *Ayrshire Collections Volume 8,* Ayr, 1966.

[282] See endnote 237.

[283] Hepar sulphuris is potassium sulphide.

[284] In 1787 William Fullarton advertised for some one to develop a kelp industry at Fullarton
(*Glasgow Mercury,* 3rd January 1787, 1b).

[285] In 1791 William Blair of Blair advertised for a manufacturer to establish a "Cotton
Work" on his estate, which was "very eligibly situated on the Water of Garnock"
where there was "twenty feet of a fall" (*Glasgow Mercury,* 29th November 1791,
384).

[286] "A pause among the speculators:" compare the fall in stock markets following the attacks
on the World Trade Centre and the Pentagon on 11th September 2001.

[287] Alnaschar wished to marry the vizier's daughter. To gain the money necessary, he
invested all that he had in a basket of glassware, but, being angry with his imaginary
wife, he kicked the basket, and broke the contents (a tale from *The Thousand and
one Nights*).

[288] The crisis in 1772 was the collapse of the Ayr Bank; see endnote 54. At the start of 1793
the gentlemen of Ayrshire agreed on "[r]esolutions of the county on the present state
of the Nation", including, as a riposte to the revolutionary ideas then current, "[t]hat
the British Constitution is the most perfect System of Government and the best
adapted to human happiness and the Prosperity of a State, of any that has ever
appeared upon Earth." Of a more practical nature were the resolutions in March
1793 concerning the manning of the Navy, internal defence, and bounties for
seamen and the West Fencibles. That April they voluntarily assessed themselves 6d
in the pound Scots for internal defence, with which no tenant was to be charged.
See Ayrshire Archives, CO3/1/4, minutes of the Ayrshire commissioners of supply.

[289] Macbeth. Act 5, Scene 5; another of the witches' prophecies is fulfilled, when Birnam
Wood advances on Dunsinane:
MACBETH: I gin to be aweary of the sun,
And wish the estate o' the world were now undone.
Ring the alarum–bell! Blow, wind! come, wrack!
At least we'll die with harness on our back.

[290] It was announced in 1793 that an application was to be made to Parliament for "liberty to
open a Canal from Riccarton bridge near Kilmarnock, to Troon harbour, on the Firth
of Clyde, and for enlarging that harbour." See *Glasgow Advertiser* 20th September
1793, 605.

[291] The first survey for the Ardrossan to Paisley canal was carried out in 1800. It was opened from Glasgow to Johnstone in 1811, and went no further. See Slaven, Anthony, *The Development of the West of Scotland 1750–1960,* London, 1975, page 34.

[292] See, for instance, Cullen, L. M., *Smuggling and the Ayrshire Economic Boom of the 1760s and 1770s,* Ayr, 1994.

[293] "The Lowland Licence Act, 1788, which was designed to curb Scotch competition for the English markets, forced a large quantity of cheap whisky on to the Scottish market, greatly increasing whisky consumption. Landowners in Scotland had opposed this measure as it would 'greatly damage the newly improved agriculture of the country, which was now geared to growing barley for the large Lowland producers and relied on supplies of draff and manure from the great distillers.'" (Moss, Michael S. and Hume, John R., *The Making of Scotch Whisky,* Edinburgh, 1981, page 48).

[294] Adam Smith, *The Theory of Moral Sentiments,* (1759); D. D. Raphael and A. L. MacFie, eds., OUP, 1976; revised reprint 1991. "Apart from its intrinsic interest as Smith's theory of ethics, this book complements *The Wealth of Nations* in its account of human nature and society. It is also easier to follow." This description, by David Campbell, is taken from the bibliography in the 1991 Everyman Library edition of *The Wealth of Nations,*

[295] By an Act of the Scottish Parliament in 1696 (A.P.S. Vol. X p. 634), the minister and heritors of every parish were required to "provide a commodious house for a school" and to supply a schoolmaster, with the cost to be met by the heritors. Similar provisions had been enacted earlier in the seventeenth century, under which schools had been established over most of central and southern Scotland, but the 1696 Act empowered the commissioners of supply of a county to act in the place of defaulting heritors and to charge them accordingly. This Act remained in effect until the Education Act of 1872 (35 & 36 Vict. c.62). Qualification as heritor was based on property rather than feudal superiority, and encompassed small landowners, such as portioners, as well as the great lairds.

[296] Fullarton's figure for the salary of schoolmasters may have been an underestimate. In 1789 the post in New Cumnock was advertised at £25 a year, with a house and schoolhouse. Applicants had to be able to teach English, Latin, writing and arithmetic. See *Glasgow Mercury,* 10th November 1789, 353.

[297] A similar opinion was expressed in the *Encyclopædia Britannica,* fourth edition (1800–10): "We will venture to say, that there is no class of men to whom a nation is so much indebted as to those employed in instructing the young: for if it be education that forms the only distinction between the civilized and the savage, much certainly is due to those who devote themselves to the office of instruction. It must be the duty therefore of every state to take care that proper encouragement be given to those who undertake this office. There ought to be such a salary as would render it an object of ambition to men of abilities and learning, or at least as would keep the teacher respectable. In Scotland, the office of a schoolmaster was formerly much more lucrative than at present, and most of that class had received liberal education; and this is the reason why the common people in Scotland have been famous even to a proverb, for their learning. But at present the salary of a country schoolmaster, independent of fees for scholars, is not greater than a ploughman can earn, being

seldom more than £8 6s 8d the consequence of which is that this, which is in fact an honourable, because an useful profession, is now sinking into contempt. It is no longer an object to a man of learning; and we must soon be satisfied with schoolmasters that can read, write, and cast accounts, a little better than the lowest of the people, or who from some natural deformity are unable to exercise a trade. And what in this case must become of the minds of the common people? They must be totally uncultivated."

[298] Sir John Sinclair was assembling the first *Statistical Account,* published in a succession of volumes from 1791 to 1799 as the various parish reports were received.

[299] To be a commissioner of supply, a landowner had to possess property with a valued rent of at least £100 Scots. Their principal function was the collection of the land tax and the administration of the valuation roll for the county, which formed the basis of assessment. They also had responsibility, in conjunction with the justices of the peace, for the maintenance of county roads, bridges and ferries, together with sundry other functions such as those relating to schools and militias. For freeholders, with a vote in parliamentary elections, the qualifying valued rent was £400 Scots.

[300] For example, Hugh Logan of Logan and Sir James Whiteford of Whiteford. A later example is Henry Campbell, 9th Earl of Loudoun, who squandered his money on the turf.

[301] The earls of Cassillis, Dumfries, Eglinton, Glasgow, Glencairn and Loudoun. After the sale of Auchincruive, Schaw Park in Clackmannanshire became the family seat of the Earls of Cathcart. Hugh Hume Campbell, 3rd Earl of Marchmont, relinquished ownership of his Cessnock estate in 1769.

[302] Frank Brady, in *James Boswell: The Later Years 1769–1795,* London, 1984, page 538, implies that Fullarton's comments on the expense of keeping up an estate refer very much to Boswell. Certainly, Fullarton had to sell his own estate.

[303] Fullarton is quoting, not quite correctly, "Essay on Man," by Alexander Pope (1688–1744). This comes from Epistle I, second stanza:
"He, who through vast immensity can pierce,
See worlds on worlds compose one universe,
Observe how system into system runs,
What other planets circle other suns,
What varied being peoples ev'ry star,
May tell why Heav'n has made us as we are.
But of this frame the bearings, and the ties,
The strong connections, nice dependencies,
Gradations just, has thy pervading soul
Look'd through? or can a part contain the whole?
Is the great chain, that draws all to agree,
And drawn supports, upheld by God, or thee?"

[304] Fullarton's "Statistical Table of the Valuation and Contents of Ayrshire" measures 16 by 17 inches. All the information from the table is presented here.

[305] 7000 yards of cloth worth in total £437 10s.

[306] Not named in the *Statistical Account* of the parish; presumed to be William Blair of Blair.

[307] For a fuller consideration of weights and measures see: "Appendix I; Scottish weights and measures 1580–1780" in Gibson, A. J. S. and Smout, T. C., *Prices, Food and Wages in Scotland 1550–1780,* Cambridge, 1995; Zupko, Ronald Edward, "The weights and measures of Scotland before the Union" in *Scottish Historical Review,* Vol. LVI, 2, No. 162, October 1977; Levitt, Ian and Smout, Christopher, "Some weights and measures in Scotland, 1843" in *Scottish Historical Review,* Vol. LVI, 2, No. 162, October 1977; and Simpson, A. C., "Measures: Interpreting Scots Measurement Units" in Pride, Glen L., *Dictionary of Scottish Building,* Edinburgh, 1996

[308] Ayrshire Archives, CO3/5/12, District of Carrick Road Minute Book 4th January 1794.

[309] The conversion factors derived from Wight's values differ from those given in "Ayrshire Weights and Measures" in *Ayrshire at the Time of Burns.*

[310] "Equivalent contemporary values of the pound: a historical series 1270 to 1999", received by the editor from the Bank of England in March 1999 and adjusted for the change in the RPI between February 1999 and January 2002 (5.9%).

[311] For information about limekilns in Ayrshire, see: Butt, John, *The Industrial Archaeology of Scotland,* Newton Abbot, 1967, pages 217–231; and Hume, John, *The Industrial Archaeology of Scotland. [Vol.] 1, The Lowlands and Borders,* London, 1976, pages 42–73.

[312] *Statistical Account,* Closeburn, Dumfriesshire. Quoted by Donnachie, Ian, *Industrial Archaeology of Galloway,* Newton Abbot, 1971, pages 145–146.

[313] Loudoun Letter Book 59, letter to H. Davidson WS, Edinburgh, 24th April 1787; quoted by Mair, *Cessnock;* see endnote 70.

[314] "English weight" would be 16 ounces to the pound and *14* pounds to the stone. Here the Trone and English systems have been confused. See page 149.

[315] Ayrshire Archives, CO3/5/22, Minute book of the Committee of the Trustees for Repairing the Roads from Irvine to Stewarton, from Irvine to Kilmarnock and from Irvine to Kilwinning, 12th June 1769 to 4th November 1784. Further information on the Ayrshire roads trustees will be found in McClure, *Tolls and Tacksmen;* see endnote 213.

[316] Major Alexander Dunlop of Aiket, in Dunlop parish, also owned Collellan, in Dundonald parish. See page 40.

Index

C

cabbage, 20, 30, 36, 43, 44, 48, 53, 58, 82, 93
calves, 37, 49, 114
Campbell, Bruce, 42, 113
Campbell, Jo., 13
Campbell, John, of Newfield, 37
Campbell, John, of Wellwood, 26, 36
Cardonnel, Mansfield, 12
carpenters, 123
Carrick, 19, 21, 73, 100, 105, 112, 115, 129, 150
carriers, 99
carrot, 20
carts, 23, 26, 36, 42, 52, 62, 85, 98, 99, 105, 106, 158
  14 cwt carried with a single horse, 26
  cost of wheels, 99
  double, 51
  single horse preferred, 98
  single horse, driven by women, 39
  too small, 40
  weighing, 99
  weight carried in, 98
cart–wright, 52
Cassillis, Earl of, 22, 100
Castle Semple Loch, 130
Cathcart, Earl of, 99
Cathcart, Sir John, 17
Catrine, 6, 130
cattle, 4, 15, 16, 19, 20, 23, 25, 31, 33, 34, 45, 49, 51, 54, 57, 61, 62, 72, 73, 75, 76, 79, 86, 89, 92, 96, 111–13, 120, 121, 158
  Alderney, 114
  Ayrshire, 112
  black, 25, 48, 76
  bleeding for sustenance, 77
  common grazing, 84
  Craven, 114
  dehorning, 112
  diseases, 115
  Dunlop, 113
  Dutch, 113
  fed potatoes, 44
  fed turnips at the stall, 28
  Galloway, 19, 112

  Guernsey, 114
  Highland, 39, 114
  Holderness, 40, 114
  horned, 43
  Irish, 114
  Lancashire, 112, 113, 114
  Lancaster, 39
  Leicestershire, 112, 114
  Lorn, 44
  milch, 48, 49, 50, 51, 79, 113, 114, 117
  neat, 111
  slaughtered, 76
  starving, 74
  tethered, 75
  various breeds, 114
  weighing, 99
Cessnock, 46, 155
checks, 127
cheese, 76, 79, 113–15
chestnut, sweet, 32
cider, 44
Clark, Patrick, of Holmes, 41
Cloncaird, 20
clover, 17, 19, 21, 25, 28, 36, 37, 38, 39, 40, 42, 43, 48, 50, 51, 53, 55, 59, 60, 62, 81, 82, 86, 90, 91, 92, 106
coal, 16, 26, 35, 44, 45, 69, 130, 131, 154
  abundance, 79
  coallieries, 75, 80
  culm, 31
  duty on coastal trade removed, 133
  manufacture of coke, 131
  pits, 31
  small, 155
  trade, 63
Cockburn, Lord, 5
cockles ("cockels"), 37
Coil. See Kyle
Coimbatore, 67
cole, 24, 82
Colebrook, Sir George, 41
Collellan ("Collan"), 40
commissioners of supply, 139, 178
Connell, Rev. James, 56
corn, 12, 14, 17, 19, 20, 21, 23, 25, 27, 28, 30, 40, 42, 43, 46, 49, 54, 57, 58,

Notes

AANHS Publications

Publications of the Ayrshire Archaeological & Natural History Society
available from Ronald W. Brash MA, Publications Distribution Manager
10 Robsland Avenue, Ayr KA7 2RW

Digging Up Old Ayr (Lindsay)	£1.00
George Lokert of Ayr (Broadlie)	£1.25
A Scottish Renaissance Household (MacKenzie)	£3.00
Plant Life in Ayrshire (Kirkwood/Foulds)	£4.20
The Barony of Alloway (Hendry)	£3.60
Robert Adam in Ayrshire (Sanderson)	£3.60
The Cumnock Pottery (Quail)	£5.00
Tolls and Tacksmen (McClure)	£3.60
Smuggling and the Ayrshire Economic Boom (Cullen)	£4.00
The Port of Ayr 1727–1780 (Graham)	£4.20
John Smith of Dalry, Part 1: Geology (ed. Reid)	£6.00
John Smith of Dalry, Part 2: Archæology & Natural History (ed. Reid)	£7.20
Mauchline Memories of Robert Burns (ed. Strawhorn) (reprint)	£3.50
Antiquities of Ayrshire (Grose, ed. Strawhorn) (reprint)	£4.20
Cessnock: An Ayrshire Estate in the Age of Improvement (Mair)	£4.50
Robert Reid Cunninghame of Seabank House (Graham)	£3.60
Historic Ayr: A Guide for Visitors, 2nd ed.	£2.50
A Community Rent Asunder:	£3.50
The Newmilns Laceweavers Strike of 1897 (Mair)	
The Rise and Fall of Mining Communities in Central Ayrshire (Wark)	£3.00
The Last Miller: The Cornmills of Ayrshire (Wilson)	£6.00
Historic Alloway, Village and Countryside: A Guide for Visitors	£2.00
The Street Names of Ayr (Close) 128 pages	£5.00
Servants in Ayrshire 1750–1914 (Aitchison) 144 pages	£5.00
Armstrong's Maps of Ayrshire (1775: reprint, 6 sheets)	£12.00